THE HYDRAULIC AGE

Public Power Supplies before Electricity

by

B. PUGH

MECHANICAL ENGINEERING PUBLICATIONS LTD
LONDON

Photoset in Great Britain by
Rowland Phototypesetting Limited, Bury St Edmunds, Suffolk
and printed by St Edmundsbury Press
Bury St Edmunds, Suffolk

THE HYDRAULIC AGE

Contents

		Page
	PREFACE	vii
One	BASIC PRINCIPLES	1
Two	ALTERNATIVE PUBLIC ENERGY SUPPLIES BEFORE THE END OF THE NINETEENTH CENTURY	15
Three	HYDRAULIC PLANT – MACHINERY AND APPLIANCES	42
Four	THE PUBLIC HYDRAULIC POWER STATIONS	91
Five	THE ELECTRO-HYDRAULIC ERA	141
	APPENDIX	
	A.1 Comparative Costs of Hydraulic and Electric Power	154
	A.2 Alternative Power Sources	160
	A.3 The Hydraulic Engineering Company Ltd, Chester	162
	A.4 Grimsby Water Tower	163
	A.5 Conversion Factors and Useful Approximations	166
	A.6 Flow of Water in Pipes	167
	A.7 Efficiency of Power Transmission	168
	A.8 Pipe Materials	170
	READING AND REFERENCE LIST	172
	INDEX	175

Preface

TODAY we accept without question Gas Boards, Electricity Boards, and Water Boards but not so long ago these essential services, now their concern, were rendered by a large number of small public utility companies. Such companies were statutory companies constituted under special Acts of Parliament. They were often purely local concerns and similar powers were frequently invested in the local authority, many municipalities having their own water, gas, and/or electricity undertakings.

It was in such times as these that in a number of large towns the public hydraulic power companies met the demand for power, and to a limited extent, for light. They set an example in public service and pioneered the trail later to be followed by the electricity companies.

It is against the background of such times that we must judge their achievements, avoiding the error so commonly made, often unconsciously, when discussing the past, of projecting backwards into the period under consideration conditions prevailing today. Victorian street scenes must be viewed under the glimmer of gas light not under the glare of floodlights. Hence when dealing with the achievements of the hydraulic companies mention is made of the alternative or competitive element to enable events to be assessed in the light of contemporary conditions.

Hydraulic power has been, and still is, used for a wide variety of purposes by such concerns as dock and harbour companies. While this is relevant and interesting the field is very wide and specialized and has been ably covered in other books. By comparison the public hydraulic companies have been neglected. We shall only briefly outline such activities in relation to the main theme and concentrate on the public companies and what they were able to offer industry and the general public.

The first of the public hydraulic power installations was at Hull and it commenced operation in 1876. The largest, and the last to survive, the London Hydraulic Power Company went into liquidation in 1976, i.e., exactly 100 years later. The peak of their prosperity occurred in the mid 1920s so it can be said they had fifty years of progress and fifty years of decline.

The author is indebted to the Institution of Mechanical Engineers and the Institution of Civil Engineers for permission to make use of material published in their Proceedings, to the Manchester and Glasgow Water Authorities, the London Hydraulic Power Co, and the Sydney Hydraulic Co, Merseyside Museums and Libraries and others who have so willingly supplied information, which wherever possible, has been acknowledged in the text.

CHAPTER ONE

Basic Principles

1.1 POWER GENERATION, TRANSMISSION, AND DISTRIBUTION

With the advent of the Industrial Revolution more and more processes previously done domestically by hand were performed by
machines in factories. These machines required power to drive
them and the cheaper that power was the lower the production
costs would be. This posed two problems (1) the generation of the
power, (2) making the power available where it was required.
Thus arose the related problems of power generation and power
transmission and distribution.

In the early days of the Industrial Revolution the sources of
power available were wind, water, and the steam engine. The
development of the first two was strictly limited by the fact that the
power had to be used where it was generated – it could not at that
time be transmitted – so the work had to be taken to the mill.

Most early factories were steam driven and the power was distributed to the various machines by belts or ropes through line
shafting (Fig. 1.1). This means of transmitting power was very
successful over short distances. It set the pattern of factory and
workshop distribution of power for many years.

In general the larger the power generating unit the more efficient
it is (provided of course that it is always worked to capacity) and
the less the operating costs per unit power generated.

An attractive proposition to reduce generating costs was to
supply a number of users with power from a central source. Not the
least of the incidental advantages was the removal of the boiler
from the power user's premises thus reducing fire risk. But
obviously such was not possible by means of belts so a new

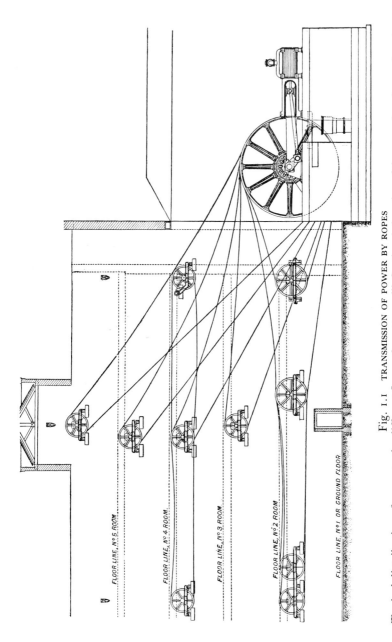

FLOOR LINE, Nº 5 ROOM.

FLOOR LINE, Nº 4 ROOM.

FLOOR LINE, Nº 3 ROOM.

FLOOR LINE, Nº 2 ROOM.

FLOOR LINE, Nº 1 OR GROUND FLOOR.

Fig. 1.1 TRANSMISSION OF POWER BY ROPES

Typical distribution of power to the different floors of a cotton mill. Sectional elevation of the rope chamber and engine house. Engine of 1100 horsepower with a flywheel 26 ft (7·92 m) diameter, grooved for 35 cotton ropes and running at 55 rev/min. Ropes 5 in (12·7 cm) in circumference. Six groups of ropes constituted the main drives, two of which each drove two intermediate shafts. From *The Steam Engine* by D. K. Clark, 1893.

approach to the transmission and distribution problem was required.

Bramah in 1802 had envisaged the use of water pressure to operate machinery. Sir William Armstrong, later Lord Armstrong, had used the domestic mains at Newcastle to operate cranes, the head of water being of the order of 200 ft (60·6 m) corresponding to a pressure of 86 lb/in² (6·06 kg/cm²).

In 1849 Armstrong was consulted regarding the use of hydraulic machinery at Grimsby Docks for the working of cranes and the operation of the dock gates and sluices. To obtain the necessary pressure he proposed to erect a tower some 200 ft in height to carry a reservoir into which water would be pumped by means of a steam engine. The machinery was ordered almost immediately but on account of various delays it did not come into operation until 1851. The result was the well-known Grimsby Water Tower. (See Appendix p. 163).

About that time Mr Fowler, later Sir John Fowler, was engaged on the construction of the ferry station of the Manchester, Sheffield and Lincolnshire Railway at New Holland on the Humber Estuary. He became interested in the application of hydraulic pressure for the operation of cranes in the goods sheds and for the raising and lowering of the platforms communicating between the railway station and the floating ferry landing stage. The ground there was flat and consisted of a dense silt incapable of providing the necessary support, so the use of a water tower as at Grimsby was ruled out, and the search for an alternative began. Air vessels in which entrapped air was compressed by the pumped-in water had been tried elsewhere and found unsatisfactory. Armstrong conceived the idea of a large cast-iron cylinder having a loaded plunger to give pressure to the water pumped into the cylinder by a pumping engine. This he called an accumulator. Although it provided a much smaller amount of power storage than a tank it enabled a much higher pressure to be used thus reducing the size of the distributing pipes and the quantity of water needed to transmit a given power. Whereas previously working pressures had not exceeded 90 lb/in² it was now decided to use a pressure of 600 lb/in².

At the New Holland station two accumulators were used, one at the pumping engine and the other at the far end of the supply pipe, the engine accumulator being slightly more heavily loaded than the other and connected with a steam regulating valve through which the speed of the engine was adjusted to meet varying demand.

After some teething troubles arising from failure of joints due to the high pressure and shrinkage of foundations, the success of the accumulator was firmly established. Immediately afterwards the same system was adopted on the advice of Fowler for the operation of cranes at the Old Dock, Great Grimsby, and the water tower was already obsolete. Following the use of the water tower at Grimsby it was proposed to erect a similar one at Birkenhead, but as soon as the superiority of the accumulator was established it was decided to adopt the new system and an accumulator system was installed there in 1851. In the same year Brunel advocated the use of hydraulic pressure for general railway station purposes and was the first to propose its use for turntables, traversers and capstans for wagon hauling.

Considerable plant of this type was installed at the Paddington Station of the Great Western Railway and this gave considerable impetus to the adoption of hydraulic machinery by railway companies.

In order to supply water at the very high pressures special hydraulic pumping engines were designed. These were basically ordinary rotative steam engines with adequate flywheels, but instead of power being taken off the crankshaft, high-pressure pumps were connected to extensions of the piston rods (Fig. 1.2). The pumps were placed either at the cover end or the crank end of the cylinder, the latter arrangement involving a divided connecting rod. The engines were built as pairs with cranks at 90°, thus avoiding a dead point and making the unit self-starting.

By the use of such hydraulic pumping engines in conjunction with hydraulic accumulators it was possible to supply water at pressures from 700 lb/in² (50 kg/cm²) upwards and thus transmit power economically over distances of up to fifteen miles, an achievement not then possible by other means. Cranes, lifts, eleva-

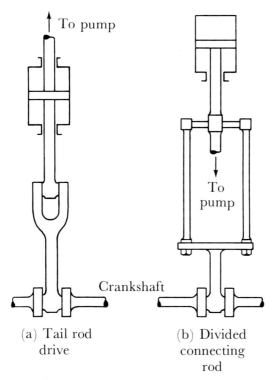

↑ To pump

To pump

Crankshaft

(a) Tail rod
drive

(b) Divided
connecting
rod

Fig. 1.2 ALTERNATIVE PUMP DRIVES
For constructional details of pumps see p. 59.

tors, and presses work on the principle of the hydraulic ram and for their operation hydraulic power had outstanding advantages. Rotative power could be efficiently obtained by the use of Pelton wheels, and piston type engines were also designed to work from hydraulic mains. The unique advantages of hydraulic power for the operation of lock gates, cranes, coal hoists, capstans, etc, were rapidly appreciated with the result that dock companies generally installed hydraulic power systems.

With the large increase in the number of relatively small power users the search for a power transmission medium by means of which power could be transmitted to a number of users from a central generating station intensified. By then hydraulic transmission stood out as the obvious choice and when hydraulic pressure was adopted as a means of supplying power to the public and industry generally the public hydraulic power companies were able to benefit from the experience of the dock and railway companies.

When public hydraulic systems were first introduced the transmission of power electrically was not considered a practical proposition with the equipment and knowledge available. It may be difficult to understand this attitude in the light of later developments but it must be appreciated that such was the generally held opinion of responsible authorities of the period.

1.3   APPRECIATION OF THE WORK OF THE SUPPLY COMPANIES

In order to appreciate the work of the public hydraulic supply companies a minimum knowledge of the rudiments of hydraulics is required and this is outlined in the next section. For the reader with some mathematical knowledge who wishes to pursue such studies further a supplementary treatment of wider scope and greater depth is available in the Appendix together with a list of suitable books for reference and/or further reading, while the non-technical reader intent on a general appraisal may omit sections 1.4, 1.5 and 1.6 on the first reading.

1.4   SOME RUDIMENTARY PRINCIPLES OF HYDRAULICS

Water is practically incompressible and transmits pressure equally in all directions. Figure 1.3 shows two cylinders (1) and (2) connected together by a pipe. Cylinder (1) contains a small diameter plunger of area a and cylinder (2) a large diameter plunger of cross-sectional area A. The whole system is filled with water. A force F applied to the plunger of cylinder (1) will result in a pressure being transmitted throughout the system so that as the plunger in cylinder (1) is pressed down the plunger in cylinder (2) will rise and lift the weight W, the volumetric displacements of both plungers being the same. The pressure in the water will be due to the force on the end only of plunger (1) since the circumferential forces on the plunger sides will balance out, so the net result

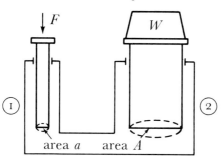

Fig. 1.3 PRINCIPLE OF THE HYDRAULIC JACK

of these will be zero. The intensity of the pressure in the water will be F/a per unit area so the force pressing upwards on the end of the plunger in cylinder (2) will be $F/a.A$ which will be equal to the weight supported, i.e., the weight W (both F and W should be inclusive of the weights of their respective plungers). In this way a small force F may be used to raise a large weight W its effect being multiplied in the ratio A/a. This is the principle of the hydraulic jack or the hydraulic ram. But the height the weight W can be lifted is very limited unless means are provided for admitting more water to the system as plunger (2) rises, and the small plunger of cylinder (1) is made to make a number of strokes, that is the small plunger functions as a pump (by means of a suitable arrangement of valves) when the large plunger of cylinder (2) becomes the ram.

The pump and ram may be a considerable distance apart. In this case water will flow continuously in the connecting pipe while the ram moves outwards. To return the ram to its original position it is necessary to shut off the supply and run water out of the ram cylinder, that is discharge the used water. So in doing the work of raising the weight W and then returning the ram to its original position a certain amount of water is used and then allowed to run to waste.

Frictional resistance has to be overcome when water is made to flow through a pipe so that some loss of pressure results.

It is often convenient to express the pressure at a point in a pipe in terms of the height to which the water would rise in an open branch pipe situated at that point and it is convenient here to express pressure p in terms of head h. The pressure at the base of a column of water of height h (Fig. 1.4) is that due to the weight of the column, i.e., wah where w is the weight of unit volume.

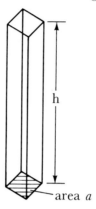

Fig. 1.4   PRESSURE EQUIVALENT TO A HEAD h

The pressure per unit area is

$$p = \frac{wah}{a} = wh, \text{ or } h = \frac{p}{w}$$

A column of water 10 m high would, at its base, exert a pressure of $1 \times 10 \times 100$ g/cm², or 1 kg/cm² which is the average pressure of the atmosphere.

The working pressure of the earlier public hydraulic power stations was 700 to 800 lb/in² (average 750 lb/in²) which corresponds to a head of

$$h = \frac{750 \times 144}{62 \cdot 5} = 1728 \text{ ft}$$

and this is the height at which the water surface would have to be in the tank of a water tower in order to provide the required pressure.

1.5   FLOW OF WATER THROUGH PIPES

Consider two points A and B distant l apart along the axis of a

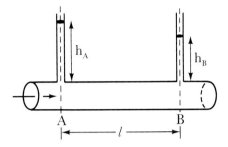

Fig. 1.5 HYDRAULIC GRADIENT

pipe in which water is flowing (Fig. 1.5). The head at B will be less than the head at A by an amount equal to the head necessary to overcome the friction resisting the flow. The loss of head per unit length of pipe is known as the hydraulic gradient, i.e., the hydraulic gradient $= (h_A - h_B)/l$. The head lost in friction at very low speeds of flow is proportional to the velocity, but at speeds met with in practice it is proportional to the square of the velocity, the change taking place at a velocity of flow known as the 'critical velocity'. It is also dependent upon the nature of the inner surface of the pipe (a rough surface causing a bigger loss of head), the length of the pipe, and the ratio of the internal circumference (i.e., the wetted perimeter) to the cross-sectional area of the pipe, which in the case of a circular pipe is

$$\frac{\pi d}{\pi d^2/4} = \frac{4}{d}$$

It can be shown that (see Appendix p. 167)

$$\frac{h}{l} = \frac{4f}{d} \cdot \frac{v^2}{2g}$$

where h is the head lost in friction and f is a constant depending upon the nature of the pipe surface.

This equation is known as Darcy's Equation. Since $p = wh$, it can be written

$$\frac{p}{l} = \frac{4f}{d} \frac{wv^2}{2g}$$

where p/l is the pressure loss per unit length of pipe, and it can be seen that the greater the pipe diameter the smaller the pressure loss per unit length of pipe.

1.6 EFFICIENCY OF TRANSMISSION AND WORKING PRESSURE

The measure of the efficiency of transmission is the proportion of the power transmitted that is available at the consumer's premises, and the greater the ratio

$$\frac{\text{Power available at consumer's premises}}{\text{Power put in at the station}}$$

the greater the efficiency. Or

$$\text{Efficiency} = \frac{(\text{Power available at the station}) - (\text{Power lost in pipe friction})}{\text{Power available at the station}}$$

For a given rate of flow the power transmitted will be proportional to the pressure, hence

$$\text{Efficiency} = \frac{(\text{Station pressure}) - (\text{Pressure drop due to friction})}{\text{Station pressure}}$$

The pressure drop between the station and the consumer will be independent of the working pressure. Hence, other things being equal, the higher the working pressure the greater the efficiency of transmission.

While the earlier stations had working pressures of 700 to 800 lb/in^2 later stations were designed to operate at half a ton (1120 lb) per square inch. A working rule was that the acceptable loss of pressure due to pipe friction was 10 lb/in^2 per mile. Hence over 15 miles the drop in pressure would be 150 lb/in^2, so for a working pressure of 750 lb/in^2 the efficiency of transmission would be $600/750 = 80$ per cent. With a working pressure of 1120 lb/in^2 the efficiency becomes $(1120 - 150)/1120 = 86 \cdot 6$ per cent.

The variation in efficiency of transmission with pipe length for the two working pressures is shown in Fig. 1.6.

It should also be noted that, for a given velocity of flow, the

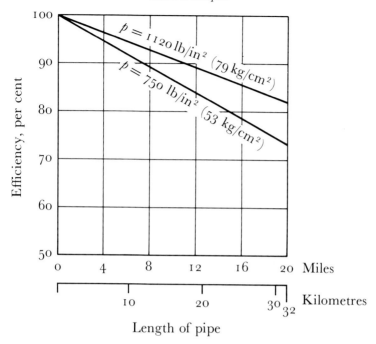

Length of pipe

Fig. 1.6 VARIATION OF EFFICIENCY OF HYDRAULIC POWER TRANSMISSION WITH
MAINS LENGTH AND WORKING PRESSURE (*p*)

higher the working pressure the greater the power transmitted in a
given pipeline, i.e., the greater the capacity of the system. But the
higher the working pressure the stronger the pipes and equipment
must be, with consequent increase in capital cost. There must also
be an upper limit imposed by practical considerations such as the
materials of construction.

It is obvious that there is a limit beyond which hydraulic
transmission becomes inefficient and it would appear to be
around 15 miles (24 km). Though this limit could be extended by
using larger diameter pipes, thus reducing the frictional loss (as
indicated by Darcy's equation) the manufacturing and mains
laying costs would be increased and it would probably be a more
economic proposition to build another station nearer the consumers to be served.

The implications are important. Since the range of a station is so limited and it is pointless to build a station bigger than is necessary to meet efficiently the power requirements of the service area, there is a limit set to the capacity of a station directly dependent upon the density of the demand in the service area.

1.7   STATION SIZE

Generally, equipment, e.g., prime movers, boilers, and even buildings, is relatively cheaper in large units than in small. The number of attendants in a large station is about the same as in a small one. In general then the larger the station, provided of course that it is efficiently working to capacity, the lower the unit cost of the power generated. We shall return to this point later but it is important to note that efficiency of transmission is of paramount importance. The early electrical stations were faced with the same difficulty (their voltage being analogous to working pressure, and voltage drop due to mains resistance analogous to pressure drop due to pipe friction) and since hydraulic power could offer some special advantages the hydraulic power stations were able to compete very successfully with them. But with the break-through in a.c. transmission and the use of very high voltages of transmission, the range of transmission of electrical power was considerably increased, large electrical power stations became a practical proposition, with consequently increased efficiency, and the decline of the hydraulic stations followed. The national grid spelt their death knell in their original form.

When a station supplies power to a number of machines, all the machines may not be in use at the same time. The generating station must be capable of meeting the full load (peak demand) and hence will be running partially loaded, or in other words relatively inefficiently, for long periods. A further advantage of a large station over a number of smaller ones lies in its ability to meet diversity of demand. A number of small independent stations must each have sufficient capacity to meet the peak demand of its own area of supply and the peaks will not all occur at the same time. A large station, however, embracing the total area of a number of small stations, will need only to meet the maximum simultaneous demand and this will normally be less than the sum total of the local peaks.

But the complete answer to the peak demand problem would be power storage. If only a.c. power could be stored the possibility of winter power cuts would not only recede considerably, but possibly disappear. If means were available whereby power could be stored during low load periods and this stored power could be drawn upon in periods of heavy demand the generating station could be powered to meet average demand which may be considerably less than the peak demand.

Some storage capacity is invaluable in meeting a sudden heavy demand which would otherwise cause a sudden drop in working pressure. Large high-pressure hydraulic accumulators do provide some storage capacity but this is small and only capable of meeting a peak demand for a matter of minutes. The main function of an accumulator is to keep the pressure steady and as its weight falls bring into action stand-by generating plant thus preventing the drop in pressure that would otherwise take place.

The obvious method of power storage is the water tower mentioned earlier, the quantity of energy stored being the weight of water in the tank multiplied by the mean height of the tank, while the working pressure is that due to the head of water. Such schemes are only possible for small installations on account of the large volume of water involved and the fact that, as shown on page 8 a tank at a height sufficient to give a working pressure of say 750 lb/in² is impossible. It is worth noting in passing, however, that a scheme similar in conception is high level lake storage used in conjunction with water turbine installations.

1.8 SPECIAL ADVANTAGES OF HYDRAULIC POWER

Hydraulic power has some outstanding advantages, so much so that although all of the public hydraulic power companies have closed down hydraulic power still continues to be used for dock purposes and to an increasing extent electrical power is converted on site to hydraulic power when, as in many cases, hydraulic operation offers special advantages.

Hydraulic operation is ideal where the requirement is linear as against rotary motion, i.e., where the ram is the basis of operation as in the case of lifts, hoists, cranes, presses, testing machines, machine tools, dock gates, etc.

1.9 USE OF DOMESTIC WATER SUPPLY

Occasionally domestic water systems have been used for the operation of hydraulic equipment. Obviously this has all the drawbacks of low pressure systems, the lower the pressure the greater the water consumption for a given power output. The water used has to be metered and must of course be available at a competitive economic rate. The water used will have been purified to drinking standards and public supplies are subject to limits so such a wastage could not be tolerated to any great extent normally and certainly not in times of drought.

CHAPTER TWO

Alternative Public Energy Supplies before the end of the Nineteenth Century

2.1 INTRODUCTION

Energy can be transmitted in various ways; also it can exist in a number of forms, one convertible to another. Mechanical energy can be transmitted by belts, ropes, chains or gears but all of these by their nature limit the distance over which the energy can be transmitted. In some cases it may be more practicable to convert mechanical to electric or hydraulic energy for convenience of transmission and convert back at the receiving end. Thermal energy in gas can be piped long distances and converted into mechanical energy where required. At the place of utilization the energy may be required for a number of purposes and in various forms. For example, energy may be needed to supply light when the possibilities are gas, direct electric supply, or a mechanical or hydraulic supply which can be readily converted to an electric supply on the site, the method ultimately to be selected depending on the relative importance of convenience and economic factors.

So in assessing the competition faced by the public hydraulic supply companies it is necessary not only to be aware of all the possible applications of hydraulic power but also of the stages reached in the development of the techniques of other methods of transmission of power, and their applications with particular reference to public power supply systems. The possibilities have changed as techniques have developed more rapidly in one field than in another and this in itself forms an intriguing study providing food for contemplation regarding developments in the future. At one time gas was predominant for lighting purposes. At another it was cheaper to transmit energy hydraulically and convert it on site to electrical energy for lighting purposes than to obtain a supply direct from a public electricity supply station. Spectacular improvements in electric generators, steam turbines, and lamps ultimately put electric lighting well to the fore while the introduction of the grid made the electrical transmission of power the predominating proposition.

In what follows an attempt is made to survey generally the prevailing state of affairs during epochs in the history of the public hydraulic power stations and to pin-point the outstanding changes in techniques which preceded the more revolutionary developments, thus providing the back-cloths against which their achievements can be highlighted.

2.2   GENERAL SURVEY

The early electric public power stations were direct or continuous current stations, the voltage of generation essentially being only slightly higher (by the voltage drop in the supply cables) than that at the consumer's premises which for safety reasons had to be less than 250 volts. The power transmitted is given by volts (V) multiplied by amps (I) while the power transmission loss is given by RI^2 where R is the resistance of the supply cable. Hence increasing the power transmitted meant increasing I and to minimize transmission losses R had to be as low as possible, which meant that supply cables had to be as short as possible. Thus the area of supply was limited as well as the amount of power that could be transmitted any distance, due to the voltage limitation.

Consequently the station capacity was extremely small judged by present-day standards, the overnight load being such that in many cases it could be met by accumulator storage. The justification for the existence of these stations was that they met the lighting demand though they offered electricity for power purposes at a lower rate than that for lighting, the consumer's lighting and power demands being separately metered. Thus they were in competition with other suppliers of power.

Although the hydraulic companies (with the exception of the special case of Antwerp) were not basically interested in the supply of power for lighting, some customers of the companies found it advantageous to generate electricity on site from the hydraulic supply, so there was an additional incidental element of competition here.

While coal-gas supplies were made available to meet the demand for better lighting, ultimately the gas engine was developed so as to become a possible competitor in the power field.

Hence our story starts, and in the early stages is bound up, with the development of good lighting at a time when good lighting was becoming both an industrial and domestic necessity. The story of lighting is in itself of fundamental interest in obtaining a true picture of contemporary living conditions. Early factory and domestic lighting was by oil or candles and these presented very serious fire hazards particularly in the case of textile factories. Gas lighting was a definite step forward, becoming more popular as burners were improved, to occupy pride of place until the arrival of the electric arc lamp followed the introduction of suitable generators. But the arc lamp was not suitable for domestic lighting and electric home and shop lighting were not possible until the introduction of the incandescent electric lamp.

It was in December 1878, some two years after the Hull Hydraulic Power Company had become operational, that Joseph Swan put on show the first practical incandescent electric lamp at a meeting of the Newcastle upon Tyne Chemical Society. The lamp had a carbon filament inside an evacuated glass bulb. Much work had gone into producing a satisfactory filament. In 1880 Swan read a paper before the Institution of Telegraph Engineers (later the IEE) on 'Incandescent Electric Light' and soon afterwards opened a factory for the manufacture of electric lamps. Previously manufacture had been on a domestic scale at the homes of Swan and a colleague called Stearn while Edison in his laboratory had been working on the same problem and had produced lamps using horse-shoe shaped filaments of carbonized paper strips enclosed in vacuum bulbs. Later Edison and Swan resolved their differences and combined forces to produce the famous Ediswan lamps.

The development of the dynamo had now reached a stage where the lighting of buildings and streets by electricity became an economic proposition in competition with gas.

Swan's house was the first to be lit by the new lamps and the next was that of Sir William Armstrong at Cragside, where a pipeline was taken from a small lake to a six-horsepower water turbine which drove a Siemens dynamo.

The main attempts to improve the electric lamp centred around the use of metal filaments, carbon filaments requiring a relatively large amount of energy to produce a given amount of light, i.e., 3 to 4 watts per candlepower. Also a carbon filament has a negative temperature coefficient of resistance as a slight increase in supply voltage produces a disproportionate increase in the current, resulting in appreciable fluctuation in brilliance of the lamp and a reduction in its life. Metal filaments have positive temperature coefficients which partly compensate for small variations in voltage. The light output from a surface depends on its temperature so the search was for a metal having a sufficiently high melting point. Thus attention was focused on the rare metals, osmium, tantalum, and tungsten. These metals have low specific resistances so very fine filaments were called for and this presented a difficulty on account of their poor ductilities, so special manufacturing techniques had to be developed. Even so filaments were long and fragile and had to be supported at a number of points.

Osmium filaments were used in 1898 and tantalum filaments appeared in 1905. Osmium filaments were replaced by those composed of an alloy of osmium and tungsten, such lamps being known as 'Osram' lamps, the syllable 'ram' being the last of the alternative name for tungsten, i.e., wolfram. Tungsten filaments followed in 1907 in the attempt to produce a higher working temperature and hence a whiter light with greater efficiency. The efficiency of a tantalum lamp was about 1·4 watts per candlepower and that of a tungsten lamp about one watt per candlepower. Methods of manufacture underwent improvements up to 1911 when lamps were filled with an inert gas permitting of the use of even higher working temperatures with resulting greater efficiency. The gas-filled lamp was known as the 'half watt lamp' because it emitted one candlepower of light per half watt of energy consumed.

Generators and Motors
The electric generator had its origin in Faraday's discovery of electro-magnetic induction (1831), i.e., that whenever a conductor is moved so as to cut the lines of force of a magnetic field an e.m.f.

is set up in the conductor. In other words if there is relative movement between a magnet and a coil of wire a current of electricity is induced in the wire.

The principle was rapidly exploited in the construction of a number of so called 'magneto-electric machines' the first of which was that of Pixii (1835), Fig. 2.1, in which the magnet A revolved close to a double coil of wire BB' in which an electric current was generated. This current changed its direction as rotation took place, so to ensure that the current always flowed in the same direction in the external circuit the extremities of the coils of wire were connected to two brass springs pressing against a rotating split brass collar, the function of which was to rectify the direction of the current produced, i.e., it changed an alternating current to a

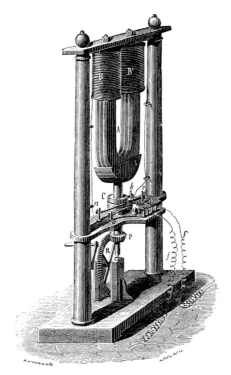

Fig. 2.1   PIXII'S MAGNETO-ELECTRIC MACHINE

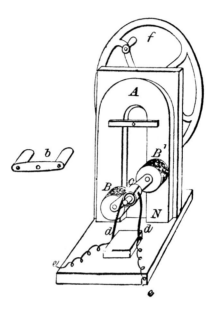

Fig. 2.2　CLARKE'S MAGNETO-ELECTRIC MACHINE
A – Horse-shoe magnet clamped to backboard. BB′ – Armature, the soft iron core of which is shown at b, rotating about its axis c and driven by a pulley behind the backboard, which in turn is driven by the flywheel f. The armature is wound with insulated copper wire, the gauge of which determines the e.m.f. generated. The ends of the wire coils are connected to the two half-cylinders which form the commutator. d and d′ are brass spring brushes. After Bottone, see Fig. 2.4.

uni-directional or 'direct' one, and it was termed a 'commutator'. This machine was improved by Saxton and later by Clarke whose machine is shown in Fig. 2.2. In this the magnet was fixed and the much lighter coils, which had soft iron cores, rotated.

If the coil ends are connected to simple collector rings instead of the segments of a commutator the current delivered will be single phase alternating which was advantageous in some circumstances.

More complex horizontal machines consisted of rings of eight horse-shoe magnets arranged symmetrically around a cast-iron frame, the rings being arranged in seven rows. In each of the six spaces between the rings rotated bronze wheels each carrying sixteen coils. Such machines, driven by steam engines, were used to operate arc lamps in several lighthouses and when used for this purpose it was advantageous to have an alternating current output since this produced uniform burning of the carbon rods of the arc light. But such machines were very bulky.

Siemens in 1864 replaced the rotating coils by his H or shuttle armature which consisted of an iron cylinder in which a deep groove was cut along its opposite sides and continued around its ends (Fig. 2.3), the coil being wound in this groove like the thread on a shuttle. Its form permitted of very rapid rotation and its relatively small size resulted in a much more compact magnet system.

Fig. 2.3   SIEMENS'S H ARMATURE
c – Soft iron cylinder. f – Brass end carrying commutator e.e. to which the ends of the winding are attached. g – Brass end carrying driving pulley.

But the field magnets used were still steel permanent magnets.* Wilde replaced the steel field magnets by soft iron electro-magnets supplied with current from a separate smaller generator which had permanent steel field magnets so the current from the smaller generator served to boost considerably the field magnetism of the main generator.

Both Siemens and Wheatstone proposed a machine in which the current produced was caused to circulate around soft iron field magnets. Iron once strongly magnetized will retain some magnetism permanently and this will serve to induce some current in the armature, which, in turn strengthens the magnetism of the field magnets so that powerful currents are quickly obtained. Machines working on this principle were called 'dynamo-electric machines' or dynamos.

* Steel when magnetized does not acquire nearly the same intensity of magnetization as soft iron but its retentitivy is much greater. The softer the iron the more powerfully magnetic it can become but the sooner it loses the magnetism imparted to it. Steel is most suitable for permanent magnets: soft iron for cores which serve to concentrate magnetism and are subject to magnetic reversals.

As previously pointed out, the direction of the current produced in the armature coils of the machines already described changes each half revolution and although it can be made uni-directional by the use of a two-part commutator the output is not continuous, like the output of a battery, but rather in the nature of rapidly succeeding half waves and a high rotational speed is necessary to ensure that the half waves succeed each other rapidly enough to produce some semblance of continuity. A much more uniform output can be obtained by the use of the ring armature with a number of independent coils around its circumference. The ring armature machine introduced by Dr Pacinotti in 1864 is shown in Fig. 2.4.

Rotation of an armature results in currents being induced not only in the armature coils but in the iron also. These currents, known as 'eddy currents' result in the heating of a solid armature

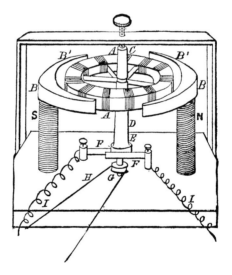

Fig. 2.4 PACINOTTI'S RING ARMATURE MACHINE
AA – Iron ring wound with coils of wire. BBB'B' – soft iron pole pieces of the electro magnets S, N. CD – axis about which the ring turns. E – Commutator to corresponding segments of which the armature coils are connected. FF – Brushes. G – Pulley driven by belt H. From *The Dynamo; How made and how used* by S. R. Bottone, 1903.

with detrimental effects both to the insulation of the coils and the intensity of magnetization. This effect was minimized in the Gramme dynamo by using a ring armature the core of which consisted of a large number of turns of soft iron wire, and in later machines by building the armature of a large number of laminations of soft iron sheet, so that the flow of the eddy currents was prevented, the armature coils being housed in longitudinal slots.

By around 1880 two leading generators incorporating the features mentioned were the Siemens, Fig. 2.5, and the Gramme, Fig. 2.6. By then the dynamo had assumed, at least in principle, its modern form, later changes being in the design of field magnets and general refinements. Early attempts at producing rotary motion electrically resulted in the so-called electric engines. These were battery operated and were little more than amusing curiosities. They had no influence on the development of the electric motor.

In general a generator will work in reverse, that is, when supplied with electricity it will produce rotary motion. Pacinotti pointed out that his machine (Fig. 2.4) would work either as a generator or as a motor and Gramme dynamos were found to operate effectively as motors.

In Part III, p. 834 of Deschanel's *Elementary treatise on Natural*

Fig. 2.5   SIEMENS'S DYNAMO-ELECTRIC MACHINE

Fig. 2.6 GRAMME'S DYNAMO-ELECTRIC MACHINE

Philosophy (1881) it is stated 'It is an interesting experiment to connect the terminals of two Gramme machines by long wires, and employ one to drive the other by means of the current produced. We thus obtain a tangible illustration of the feasibility of transmitting power from one station to another by the intervention of electricity. The time will probably come when the power of waterfalls and rapids will thus be conducted to places where it can conveniently be utilized.'

Such was the position regarding the electrical transmission of power in 1881 when the Hull Hydraulic Power Company had been operational for some five years. It was in these circumstances that the dismal contemporary prophecies regarding the future of electrical transmission and distribution of power were made.

2.3 COAL GAS

Gasification of coal, i.e., heating of coal out of contact with air, permits of the transmission of the resulting energy by pipes.

Instead of existing in the form of pressure energy as in hydraulic and pneumatic systems the energy resides in the chemical constitution of the gas and is released as heat when the necessary oxygen for combustion is made available at the point of delivery. Like electrical supplies gas supplies were initially intended to provide light.

William Murdock, while in the employ of James Watt in 1792, lit his house in Redruth by means of coal gas and in 1802 lit the Soho foundry by the same means. But he was concerned with the lighting of individual buildings and not a public supply. In 1812 a Royal Charter was granted to form a company for the lighting of streets in Westminster, the company being named the Chartered Gas Company which later became the Gas Light and Coke Company, now the largest and oldest gas undertaking in the world. By the middle of last century there were gas supplies in most of the large towns in Great Britain.

Coal gas without any previous admixture of air burns with a yellow flame. During the course of combustion under such conditions carbon is liberated from the hydrocarbon constituents and the particles of carbon become incandescent in the hot flame, this incandescence being the source of the light emitted. Several types of burner to consume gas under these conditions were available, such as the batswing, fish-tail, and Argand burners.* In 1869 the Board of Trade appointed Gas Referees to assess gas quality in the London metropolitan area. They appraised the illuminating quality of gas by the light given out by a specially designed Argand burner.

Gas lighting was revolutionized by the invention of the Bunsen burner and the fact that oxides of certain rare metals acquire a high luminosity when heated in a flame. In the bunsen burner air is

---

* The fish-tail and batswing were open flat flame burners. The Argand burner (named after its inventor) gave a cylindrical flame which was enclosed in a glass chimney.

The fish-tail had a steatite concave top with two outlets at such an angle that the gas jets united to form a flame somewhat like the tail of a fish. The batswing had a hemispherical steatite top with a narrow vertical slot from which the issuing flame resembled a bat's wing. The Argand burner had a hollow steatite ring perforated around its upper edge with fine holes from which the gas issued to give the cylindrical flame.

mixed with the gas before combustion thus greatly increasing the rate of combustion. As a result free carbon particles are not formed and the flame is practically non-luminous. If a mantle of oxides of rare metals is placed over the flame the high temperature will cause the mantle to become incandescent.

The mantles may be made of a suitable textile, e.g., artificial silk, which is impregnated with a solution of nitrates of cerium (1 per cent), and thorium (99 per cent). After drying, the mantle is heated when the textile is burnt away leaving a fine network of oxides of cerium and thorium. The gas mantle was invented by Von Welsbach in 1885.

The introduction of the mantle and the aerated burner made the old flat flame burners obsolete and whilst previously the quality of gas was assessed by its illuminating power the criterion now became the calorific value since the light given out by a mantle is dependent purely on the heating of the mantle. Thus the calorific value of the gas became the essential factor for lighting as well as heating of all kinds, and gas, like electricity, became marketable on an energy basis.

As gas lighting declined in the face of electrical competition, gas became more widely used for heating, both domestic and industrial, and process work as well as being available for the supply of mechanical power by means of the internal combustion engine or the gas turbine. With the exploitation of North Sea gas, its use increased to an almost embarrassing extent, but this is proceeding beyond the period of immediate interest. The main point is that the gas supply industry, like the electricity supply industry, began by attempting to supply the lighting demand but later developed as a means of supplying power, in competition with the hydraulic power stations, albeit in the case of gas to a limited extent via the gas engine.

A big advantage of a gas supply as an energy source is that gas can be stored in large quantities and drawn upon as required.

Gas and Oil Engines
The gas engine has many apparent advantages over the steam engines as a prime mover. The absence of a boiler means a reduction in space occupied and capital cost, and there is no

waiting time to get up steam. Although a number of gas engines had been devised by earlier pioneers the credit for introducing the first practical working gas engine belongs to Lenoir. He took out patents in Britain and France in 1860 and the manufacture of engines was commenced in both countries. During the first year units of six and twenty horsepower were built. Its obvious advantages coupled with unfounded claims to outstanding economy resulted in a large initial demand for the engine so that in five years between three and four hundred engines were built in France and one hundred in Britain. The claim made for it that it was more economical than the steam engine could not be substantiated, trials indicating that the average consumption for small powers was 106 cubic feet of gas per horsepower hour. Reaction to initial enthusiasm set in with the result that its faults were over-emphasized and the engine fell from favour. But it had served to draw attention to the advantages of the gas engine and to focus attention on the ways in which its performance could be improved, and much attention was devoted to improving performance. Beau de Rochas found the key to a substantial improvement in efficiency, pointing out the necessity to compress the gaseous mixture before

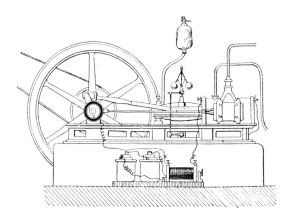

Fig. 2.7   LENOIR GAS ENGINE 1860

Double acting. Electric ignition. No compression of charge. Charge of gas and air admitted during first half of stroke, then cut off and ignited. Air/gas ratio approximately 12 to 1.

igniting it, but it was not until 1876 that Otto made a successful engine incorporating this principle. The engine was exhibited at the Paris Exhibition of 1878 and it very soon dominated the field. The gas engine using town gas had arrived. More than 30 000 engines were sold in the first ten years. A trial on a 4 horsepower Otto engine in 1881 gave a gas consumption of 28·3 cubic feet per i.h.p. hour which assuming a mechanical efficiency of 85 per cent works out at 33 cubic feet per b.h.p. hour and this was halved for larger engines towards the end of the century. Improvements in the engine soon resulted in decreased gas consumption but such figures as are available can only be taken as approximate as they varied with the size of the engine and there was considerable variation in the calorific value of the lighting gas of the period.

The first commercially successful oil engine which used a vaporizer was invented by Priestman in 1888. The Hornsby

Fig. 2.8 OTTO SILENT GAS ENGINE 1876

Four-stroke cycle. Flame ignition. Compression ratio 3 to 1. Air/gas ratio approximately 12 to 1. Combined admission and ignition control valve. Cam-operated exhaust valve.

A Water jacketed cylinder	B Piston lubricator.
C Centrifugal governor.	D Slide valve lubricator.
E Ignition gas jet chimney.	F Spring loading on slide valve.

from *Elementary Treatise on Natural Philosophy* by A. Privat Deschanel. Part II 1881.

Ackroyd engine using fuel injection was introduced in 1894, thus marking the birth of the heavy oil engine, and a year later Diesel made his first engine.

Gas engines were used to generate electricity for private house electric lighting towards the end of the last century, often being accommodated in the basement or an outhouse, and many cinemas obtained an electricity supply in the same way. Oil engines met with some popularity for the same purpose in country districts and gas and oil engines often supplied the motive power for smaller factories.

Gas supply companies were far more numerous than hydraulic supply companies but information is lacking regarding the extent to which gas companies met the demand for power or to what extent they were in direct competition with the hydraulic power companies.

2.4   STEAM

The conversion of the chemical energy in coal or other primary fuel into heat energy stored in steam involves the use of a boiler. Some of the types of boiler available are briefly described in Chapter 3. The steam engine was one of the earliest means of supplying power but in the case of small factories it was often a wasteful and sometimes a dangerous method. When power was required inter-mittently a head of steam had to be maintained continuously. One of the advantages claimed for public power supplies was that they supplied power only when it was required and they were thus more economical than a steam plant on site. Also the fire hazard inherent in the use of a steam boiler, particularly where the boiler could not be housed in a separate boiler-house, was removed.

The Birmingham Compressed Air System was inaugurated in order to supply compressed air to a large number of small existing steam engines thus doing away with the boiler hazard and avoiding the necessity of purchasing new power units since small steam engines would operate on compressed air. But the question might well be asked, why not a public steam supply? A public steam supply would remove the fire risk associated with a boiler on the premises while providing some unique advantages. But it has disadvantages. Unlike a hydraulic system a steam supply system involves a loss of heat as well as a loss of pressure energy involved in pushing the steam through the supply pipes since the temperature of the steam must be well above ambient temperature.

A public steam supply system was available in New York in the 1880s and had the advantage that not only was the energy available for power purposes but it could be used for the heating of buildings and process work. Two companies originally started to supply steam in New York. One company used cast-iron pipes but these burst and the project was abandoned. No reasons for the failure are available. The other company used wrought-iron pipes with flexible joints which proved a success. The steam was transmitted through the streets at a pressure of 90 lb/in^2 in mains 16 and 11 in diameter, and the pressure drop along the mains proved to be surprisingly low. The service was of considerable utility allowing boilers, coal and gas fires to be dispensed with and the steam was also used for cooking.

2.5 COMPRESSED AIR SYSTEMS

Fundamental Principles

Compressed air was, in the early years, the most serious rival of hydraulic power transmission and several public compressed air systems were inaugurated. Much experience in the use of compressed air had previously been obtained in mining and tunnelling. It is of some interest briefly to compare the merits of the two methods of power transmission.

Water is practically incompressible so a force applied to a quantity of water is uniformly distributed in all directions. Water in hydraulic transmission systems has been likened to a rigid rod between the pump and motor or other appliance. Air, however, is compressible and introduces flexibility. It acts much the same as a compression spring between the compressor and motor, that is it can store up internal energy, which is in the form of heat showing itself in a rise in temperature. If air is compressed very slowly the internal energy is low and the rise in temperature slight. If, however, the compression is quick the rise in temperature is high and then provision is usually made to get rid of the heat generated during compression. When the temperature remains constant the compression is called isothermal compression. When no heat is abstracted during compression the compression is said to be adiabatic.

Compressed air moving from one point to another will be rapidly cooled by its surroundings if it has not already been cooled to ambient temperature, that is, the heat added to the air during compression and not then abstracted is soon lost in the process of transmission and this heat represents a definite loss of power.

On reaching the consumer a quantity of compressed air is capable of doing work not only by virtue of its pressure, but it can also be used expansively in the same way as steam, and in this way a pneumatic system has an advantage over a hydraulic system in that water under pressure cannot be used expansively. But as compressed air expands its volume increases and the pressure and temperature fall so that if air entering an engine in which it is used expansively is originally at room temperature, after expansion it will be below room temperature. It has been claimed that in a hot climate the ejection to the atmosphere of cold air is a definite advantage and that the air can be used for refrigerating purposes. If, however, any moisture is present, as it often is, then ice forms at the exhaust port causing blockage, and this was at one time a source of trouble. Ice formation at the exhaust can be overcome by preheating the air and air heaters were available from compressed air supply companies for heating air on the consumer's premises. It was found that such preheated air was capable of doing more work than an equal quantity of unheated air. Very high efficiencies were claimed in cases where the air had been preheated on consumers' premises, but on investigation it has been shown that such claims were fallacious in that the calculations did not take into account on the debit side the energy added to the air in the form of heat in the preheater.

A simple hydraulic motor cylinder has to be completely filled with water regardless of the load to be overcome, but in an air engine a variable volume can be used and after the supply has been cut off by the engine valve gear, the air, by expanding, will continue to do work. Thus the point of cut-off can be varied to suit the load and the power output required, with a consequent considerable saving in working fluid. The significance of this did not, however, entirely escape the notice of hydraulic engineers and several compromise solutions went at least part of the way to diminishing the relative disadvantage. These are described in Chapter 3 which deals with hydraulic machinery.

Should the air be preheated before it enters the engine cylinder then the volume of a given amount of metered air is increased so less metered air will be required to perform a given amount of work, but the advantage will be off-set by the extra cost of the fuel burnt in the preheater. Further advantages of compressed air systems are that air costs nothing whereas unless an adequate supply is available water has to be purchased and even when adequate supplies are available filtration and purification costs are involved. Exhaust air can be returned direct to the atmosphere whereas exhaust water must run to waste or an expensive return flow system must be installed, but a hydraulic system offers the not insignificant advantage that pressure water operating special hydrants provides a valuable means of fighting fires and an additional public service the benefits of which were demonstrated on a number of occasions.

Transmission losses were much smaller with compressed air than with hydraulic systems and a compressed air system had a special appeal in industrial areas where a large number of small steam engines had been in operation and the compressed air supply replaced the steam boiler. This was the case in Birmingham.

In general, working pressures in compressed air systems were very much lower than those in hydraulic systems. The effects of a leaky compressed air main would appear to be less serious than in the case of hydraulic systems though in practice leaks in the mains of hydraulic systems did not have very serious consequences.

The range of appliances available for air operation was very similar to that for hydraulic systems though lifts and cranes would be operated by air-driven hydraulic pumps.

Birmingham compressed air system
The object of this scheme was 'to substitute compressed air for steam for driving the numerous small or moderate sized factory

engines in the district'. An Act of Parliament was obtained to permit conveyance of the compressed air in mains through the principal streets of the district and from these mains service pipes were taken to the various consumers. The district authorized by the Act comprised the wards of Deritend, St Martin, St Bartholomew, and Bordesley but at first activities were confined to the first three. The site of the Air Compressing Works was a triangular piece of land lying between the Midland Railway, the Birmingham and Warwick Canal, and Garrison Lane. The district served was bounded by the Midland Railway as far as Belgrave Street, Belgrave Road to Bristol Street, then Broomsgrove Street, Jamaica Row, Moor Street, Coleshill Street, Belmont Row, Lawley Street, and Garrison Lane back to the works, the total area being about one and a half square miles. The total length of the mains was about 23 miles, the diameter varying from 24 in to 7 in. The mains were of wrought iron laid in concrete troughs with removable covers as near as possible to the surface of the road. The air was metered through meters similar in construction to Beales Gas Exhauster fitted with a mechanism to correct the reading for any variation in the pressure of the supply.

The works was laid out for an output of 15000 gross indicated horsepower of which 6000 was initially installed in 1886.

Coal was gasified in 31 eight-hundredweight producers and the gas was fed to boiler furnaces, the producers being governed by the air pressure. When the air pressure rose the steam injection to the gas producers was reduced and the fires under the boilers thereby lowered and vice versa.

Forty-five Lane's Patent water-tube boilers were provided for in sets of three to each engine house. Fifteen engine houses were provided for, built in rows, in the spaces between which the boilers were erected. Each engine house was to contain one triple-expansion beam air-compressing engine of 1000 horsepower driving six single-acting air-compressing cylinders coupled to opposite ends of the beams and capable of delivering 2000 cubic feet of air per minute at 45 lb/in^2 above atmospheric pressure. The air intake was through casings from the top of each engine house in which were inserted filtering screens. Feed, condensing, and air cooling water which could have totalled six million gallons per day when the station was fully operational, was drawn from the canal at one end of the works and returned at a point four hundred feet farther on.

Paris compressed air system

In 1881 the Municipality of Paris granted to M. Victor Popp permission to establish one or more central stations and to lay mains in the first, second, third, fourth, eleventh, and nineteenth arrondisements of Paris with the object of operating a system of pneumatic clocks in the streets, and it was the intention ultimately to extend the system from the public service to private users.

The first station was completed in 1881 upon the heights of Belleville in the Rue St Fargeau. It contained engines and compressors with a total output of 80 horsepower together with the necessary receivers and ancillary plant. The company was entitled the Compagnie Parisienne de l'Air Comprimé (Procedes Victor Popp), the agreement being signed on 14 September 1881 by the Prefect of the Seine on behalf of the Ville de Paris, the company being required to pay the Municipality a proportion of their revenues in return for the use of subways and streets and the right to lay new mains and service pipes.

At the central station a standard clock operated every minute a valve connected to a compressed air receiver allowing air to pass into the mains for the first 20 seconds of every minute and permitting the air to escape to the atmosphere during the next 20 seconds. The clock mechanism consisted of a bellows which by successively expanding and contracting imparted motion to a connecting rod with a pawl attached to its end. This pawl actuated a ratchet wheel having 60 teeth so this wheel made one complete revolution every hour, and the minute hand of the clock was attached to its spindle. A second pawl was necessary to prevent the ratchet wheel moving backwards. The hour hand was driven in the usual way from the minute hand spindle through reduction gearing. Some clocks were fitted with a bell for striking the hours, the clockwork operating mechanism being gradually wound by each stroke of the bellows.

The agreed specially reduced tariff charged by the company for the maintenance of the public clocks was not sufficient to make the service remunerative, but it was anticipated that the private demand for clocks would make the system profitable. The clocks became popular and the possession of a pneumatic clock became a status symbol.

It was soon found that the power produced was in excess of that required to operate the clocks. Investigations were made into the feasibility of supplying compressed air for power purposes, resulting in the granting of a second concession to the Popp Company in 1886, and this gave the company the right to lay and maintain a system of mains for the distribution of compressed air for motive power purposes to any point within the boundary of Paris, the Ville de Paris claiming 30 per cent of the net profits.

The extension of the works at St Fargeau was commenced soon after the signing of the new agreement. By 1887 the engine and compressor house was a rectangular structure 100 m long and 20 m wide with an adjoining boiler house 20 m long and 11 m wide. The first engine erected was a beam engine of 350 horsepower built by M.M. Casse et Cie of Lille. The completed extensions of 1887 contained a series of six engines supplied by Davey Paxman & Co, each able to develop 400 horsepower at a speed of 50 rev/min giving a total output for this part of the installation of 2400 horsepower. The air compressors, also supplied by Davey Paxman, were installed on the same bedplates as the engines and were driven from the engine piston rods. The air from the compressors passed into seven receivers arranged end to end along a wall, it being possible to isolate any receiver for repair purposes. Each receiver, cylindrical in form, was 12½ metres long and 2 metres in diameter. The boilerhouse contained thirteen boilers each with a heating surface of about 1100 ft².

Extensions completed in 1889 made provision for five additional engines and compressors, and a boilerhouse containing ten boilers, this plant being supplied by the Cockerill Company (see plan Fig. 2.9). The rest of the available space was occupied by offices, repair shops, and a meter testing room. In the plan, AA shows a Farcot engine and two compressors, BB is the second Farcot engine and two similar compressors. Farcot engines were horizontal Corliss type pumping engines, the total horsepower of the two engines being 120. This was the plant installed for the pneumatic clock

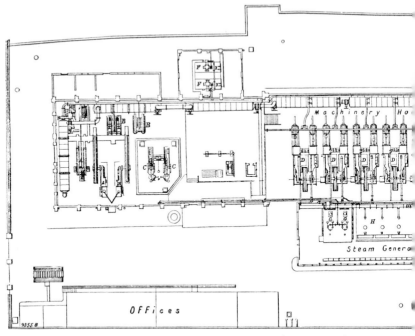

Fig. 2.9   THE DISTRIBUTION OF COMPRESSED AIR AT PARIS (POPP SYSTEM); WORKS AT
ST. FARGEAU. From *Engineering*, 1889

system. C is the air compressing engine by M.M. Casse, DD the six
engines and compressors supplied by Davey Paxman & Co, while
EE shows the five engines and compressors by Societé Cockerill.
The boilers supplying the Farcot engines are shown at F, those
supplying the Davey Paxman engines at HH while those supplying
the Cockerill engines are shown at KK. The whole installation was
lit by electricity generated on site. A subway gave access from the
works to the system of underground tunnels which traversed Paris
and in which the mains were laid whenever possible.

Before use on a consumer's premises the air passed through a
pressure regulator, the function of which was to reduce the
pressure somewhat in order to maintain the pressure reasonably
uniform and avoid transmitting to the motors the slight variations
in pressure which existed in the mains from time to time. From the
regulator the air passed to the meter recording the air used on the

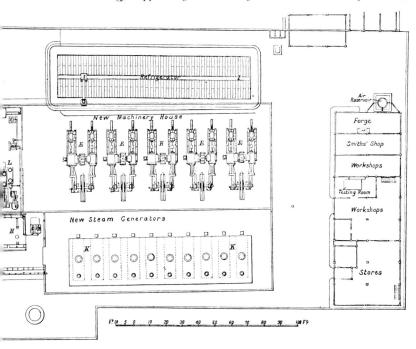

premises. The motors used were of a special type designed by the company and supplied to the consumer by direct purchase, deferred payments, or straight hire, in sizes from small motors for sewing machines to engines of 100 horsepower.

The air was supplied at a mean pressure of 45 to 70 lb/in² and the charge was 1½ centimes per cubic metre reduced to atmospheric pressure.

It was found that the demand for power could be grouped into that from industry lasting from eight in the morning to six in the evening, that for the generation of electricity for lighting – a variable demand according to the season, being from six in the evening in summer to five the following morning, and in winter from four in the evening to two the following morning with a diminished demand until daylight, and the constant demand for the pneumatic clocks.

In 1889 plans were made to increase the total output of the central station to 6000 horsepower. At that time the output was fed to seven generating stations for the purpose of supplying electricity for public lighting, representing a total demand of 750 horsepower, by air motors of which six were of 100 horsepower each. Consumers included theatres, cafes, restaurants, hotels, newspaper offices, etc, the uses including lift operation, metalworking, pumping wines and spirits, ventilation, ice-making, driving mills, private house electric lighting, and to a large extent driving woodworking machinery, and it was anticipated that the company would be able to pay a regular dividend of 10 per cent.

For factory and domestic use the system had the big advantage that the expanded air, after having done its work, could be released directly into the room where the engine was at work. Domestic applications included the generation of electricity on site for lighting, the driving of sewing machines and other light machinery, and a push-button which was virtually a conical seating springloaded valve, could be used to control the supply of air to a bell or other audible calling device.

2.6   THE EARLY ELECTRIC POWER STATIONS

A good overall picture of the state of affairs in the early days of the public power stations can be obtained from the proceedings of the professional institutions. While the task of wading through the proceedings is rewarding it is also laborious. A concise summary of the papers read before the Institution of Mechanical Engineers in the latter half of the nineteenth century is given in the official history of the Institution.

At the Summer Meeting of the Institution of Mechanical Engineers, held in Paris in 1878 a paper was read on Electric Lighting. The only method of lighting then available was the arc lamp, as the incandescent lamp had not been invented. Five hundred industrial works in France were using arc lighting, the usual industrial lighting generator absorbing 2·5 horsepower at 850 rev/min. The first public lighting by electricity was that of Billingsgate Market in 1878.

In 1881, during a general discussion on power transmission the opinion was expressed that compressed air and hydraulic transmission were to be adopted when power had to be widely distributed, but electric transmission should be the last consideration. It was further stated that there was very little scope for improvement in the efficiency of electric generators. By 1888 the largest dynamo in the world was one of 500 h.p. At the Summer Meeting of the Institution of Mechanical Engineers that year Sir Charles Parsons described his invention in a paper illustrated by drawings of turbo-generators of 16 and 32 kilowatt capacity.

The Presidential Address of the Institution in 1894 was delivered by Sir Alexander B. W. Kennedy who was chief engineer of the Westminster Electricity Corporation and designer of its three principal stations, and whose opinion therefore is to be accepted as authoritative in the light of the conditions then prevailing and is of further interest as indicating the state of the opposition at about the time when the public hydraulic power stations were at their heyday, London having been in existence since 1883 and Manchester since the beginning of 1894, while Glasgow was to open in 1895.

He considered that the main business of the electric power stations was to supply current for lighting, and he doubted whether it would ever be a paying proposition to build a station in a manufacturing district to supply power to factories. As regards station size, the Davies Street Station of the Westminster Company had a maximum peak load of 775 kilowatts in 1893. The Dickinson Street station of Manchester Corporation in the same year had a rated capacity of 1320 kilowatts, the power being supplied by ten engines each driving a dynamo through a link belt, steam being supplied by six Lancashire boilers working at 125 lb/in². The Oldham municipal station started in 1894 with four Willans engines of 80 h.p. each, steamed by two Lancashire boilers and driving 100 volt dynamos. During the hours of small demand the total load was taken by batteries.

The Edinburgh municipal station opened in 1895 had a total d.c. output of 1000 kilowatts, supplied by eight units, with a battery of accumulators, and supplemented by two 80 kilowatt single-phase alternators for supplying the outlying districts of the city. Steam was supplied at 160 lb/in².

During the same year (1894) in Melbourne, Australia, where a hydraulic power supply system was established in 1887, the Electric Light Station, situated in Spencer Street, consisted of an engine room, boilerhouse, fitting shop, engineer's residence, and lamp testing room. The engine room had four sections each containing a compound surface condensing engine of 300 indicated horsepower driving a countershaft 30 ft long, making a total length of countershaft of 120 ft, the component lengths being connected by clutches. Five dynamos for arc lighting were driven off each sectional countershaft. Steam was supplied by Babcock and Wilcox boilers at 150 lb/in^2. In this case the demand seems to have been limited solely to street lighting.

The average price of electricity at that time in the United Kingdom was 6d (2½ p) per Board of Trade Unit (kilowatt-hour). It was forecast then that 'in the near future' electric lighting would become as cheap as gas. The big advantage claimed for electric lighting was that unlike gas it did not vitiate the atmosphere and consequently was much more desirable from the health aspect. Mr W. H. Preece is reported as saying that through the lighting of the London Post Office by electricity the absence due to sickness was so diminished that the value of the services thus made available was equal to the cost of the light, so that the electric light virtually paid for itself.

With the introduction of the incandescent lamp the benefits of electric light became more apparent and the question prominent in the minds of potential users was whether to generate the electricity on site or to obtain a supply from the local lighting station. To a limited extent electricity was generated on site by steam or gas engines but, except where no alternative existed the drawbacks were obvious. However, where a public hydraulic power supply was available it was clean and convenient to use such a supply to generate electricity for lighting and it was also found in a number of cases to be cheaper than obtaining a supply from the local electricity station. So for a short time at least, the public hydraulic power stations were able to compete successfully with the electric stations in their own specialized field as well as being able to offer an efficient power supply. The triumph of the public hydraulic power stations was complete. But it was of short duration. Spectacular developments in electric power generation and distribution were about to take place. The extent and impact of these is the subject of a later chapter. Meanwhile, by the end of the nineteenth century, the public hydraulic power stations which form our main theme had, after some twenty years of public service, gained supremacy over all their competitors and they were to go on to render many more years of good service in the supply of power. Their rise, equipment, history, and demise form the subjects of the next two chapters.

The background picture we have to bear in mind as a summary of this section is that as the end of the nineteenth century approached many towns had their own direct-current electricity generating stations of very small capacity by present day standards, i.e., round about 1000 kilowatts, meeting mainly the demand for lighting, with a night load such that it could be met by accummulator storage. Alternating-current generation and distribution, to play a predominant part. in later developments, was then in its infancy.

CHAPTER THREE

Hydraulic Plant – Machinery and Appliances

3.1 INTRODUCTION

It is not possible in a small work of this type to portray the evolution of the steam pumping engine or even to detail the design of all the various engines then available to the designers of the early hydraulic power stations. Nor are these essential to a general appreciation of the work of the public hydraulic power companies. The object of these brief notes is to give the interested layman with no technical knowledge a general picture of the equipment in use at the time and to elucidate the nomenclature used.

3.2 PUMPING ENGINES

The simple slide valve rapidly became the general means of controlling the flow of steam into and out of the engine cylinder. In the simple steam engine all the expansion of the steam takes place in the one cylinder, and with a slide valve the same ports are used by live and exhaust steam alternately (Fig. 3.1). A high expansion ratio, necessary to abstract the maximum possible energy from

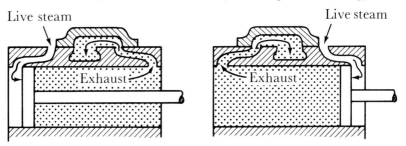

Fig. 3.1 FLOW OF STEAM THROUGH CYLINDER PORTS

high-pressure steam, means a high temperature difference between live and exhaust steam, since during expansion, as the pressure falls so does the temperature, so hot and relatively cold steam is passing alternately through the same ports, alternately heating and cooling the metal, and consequently considerable condensation loss of live steam is inevitable. To reduce this condensation loss the expansion can be made to take place in stages, that is, in more than one cylinder, so we have compound (two cylinders, the smaller being the HP (high pressure) and the larger the LP (low pressure)) or triple (three cylinders of increasing size HP, IP (intermediate pressure), and LP) expansion engines. The greater the initial steam pressure, and the higher the expansion ratio, the greater the plant efficiency, but the more the stages of expansion to keep the temperature drop per stage within given limits.

We have seen that, in order to avoid a dead point, that is a position where there is no turning moment, as occurs in a single-cylinder engine when the crank and connecting rod are in line, it is necessary to have two cranks, and these at right-angles, and hence at least two cylinders. With a low boiler pressure two cylinders each taking live steam can be used, but with higher pressure steam, compound working is highly desirable and automatically gives the necessary two cylinders. Very large compound engines may have two LP cylinders in parallel each having half the volume of the equivalent single LP cylinder which would otherwise be unduly large (see Fig. 3.2).

The earliest steam engines were used for pumping purposes and much attention had been given to pumping problems by the time the problem of supplying water under pressure arose, so a considerable amount of accumulated experience was available. The rotative steam engine with the pump directly connected to the piston rod had evolved as the result of waterworks practice and was the obvious immediate choice. (Later, for specialist purposes, direct-acting steam pumps were made but these were not used in the hydraulic power stations.) The rotative steam engine had reached a high state of development with relatively high pressures in use and compound and triple expansion engines had been developed to obtain the maximum economy in the use of high-pressure steam by expansive working. Also a large number of

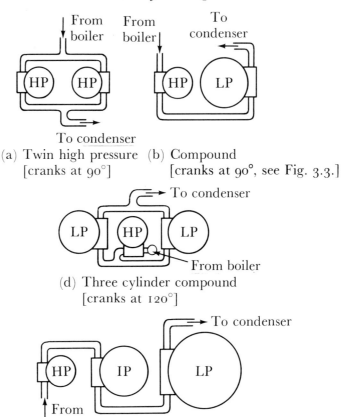

(a) Twin high pressure (b) Compound
  [cranks at 90°]   [cranks at 90°, see Fig. 3.3.]

(d) Three cylinder compound
[cranks at 120°]

(e) Triple expansion [cranks at 120°]

Fig. 3.2 PUMPING ENGINE TYPES

special valve gears had been invented and successful valve gears were available by which the expansion ratio could be varied during running, permitting of a measure of flexibility so that maximum economy under normal working conditions was possible but extra power could be obtained when the demand warranted it.

Since the rotative pumping engine was but a modification of the rotative engine, designers could take full advantage of this accumulated knowledge.

This has of necessity to be very brief, sufficient only to get the major developments in their proper perspective.

The first compound steam engine was built by Jonathan Hornblower in 1781, though the idea of compounding did not become popular until the middle of the nineteenth century. Compound pumping engines were installed in the Lambeth waterworks about 1850. In marine practice where economy of fuel is of even greater importance than in land practice the compound principle was rapidly extended to triple and quadruple expansion engines. Increasingly larger engines were built, ten thousand horsepower from one set of engines being not uncommon, and some outstanding efficiencies were obtained. There was no demand for hydraulic pumping engines of this large size, but this is quoted as indicating the progress made in the development of the reciprocating steam engine by the beginning of the present century.

Relevant dates, mentioned elsewhere but collected here for convenience, are: hydraulic accumulator invented 1851, public hydraulic stations inaugurated, at Hull 1876, at London 1884, at Liverpool 1888, at Melbourne 1889, at Manchester 1894, and at Glasgow 1895.

It is convenient here to make a brief mention of the steam turbine. In 1884 the Hon. Charles Parsons took out his first patent for what then became known as the Parsons Compound Turbine. For some time it was made in small sizes, discharging directly into the atmosphere, i.e., it was non-condensing and consequently its efficiency was low.

In 1891 Parsons modified his turbine for use with a condenser so that it was able to make the maximum use of the energy of the steam right down to the best vacuum possible in the condenser. Then began its use on a much larger scale particularly as a prime mover in electricity supply stations. At that time Professor Ewing reported that the efficiency of the Parsons turbine was comparable with that of a good reciprocating compound engine of the same capacity, but it was not long before these figures were improved upon and turbines of a much larger size built. The constructional simplicity, compactness, and freedom from vibration of the tur-

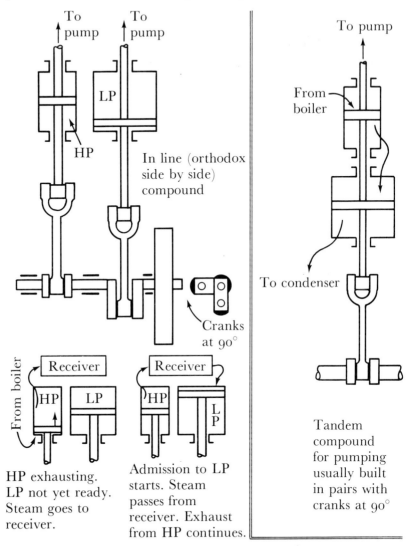

To ↑ pump   To ↑ pump

LP

HP

In line (orthodox side by side) compound

Cranks at 90°

From boiler

Receiver

From boiler HP   LP

HP exhausting. LP not yet ready. Steam goes to receiver.

Receiver

HP   L P

Admission to LP starts. Steam passes from receiver. Exhaust from HP continues.

To pump

From boiler

To condenser

Tandem compound for pumping usually built in pairs with cranks at 90°

Receiving capacity is essential, but not necessarily a separate vessel. Usually in practice the HP exhaust pipe and LP valve chest provide sufficient capacity.

Fig. 3.3   COMPOUND ENGINE TYPES

bine were rapidly appreciated and it ultimately became predominant as the large prime mover. The means of generating very high powers had arrived. But to take advantage of it the means of transmitting and distributing large powers over wide areas was required. This ultimately came in the form of high-voltage alternating-current electricity but meanwhile the hydraulic power stations did their part in helping to meet the power requirements of the general public in the first Hydraulic Age.

3.4 SOME VITAL STATISTICS

The various types of cylinder arrangement are shown diagrammatically in Fig. 3.3 while Fig. 3.4 shows a very early hydraulic pumping engine. Following are details of some of the engines manufactured by the Hydraulic Engineering Co of Chester at the turn of the century, and these will serve to give some idea of the size and type of equipment available. All were capable of pumping against an accumulator pressure of 750 lb/in^2.

The horizontal type engine appears to have been popular with the dock companies and examples are:

(1) Tandem compound with cylinders 20, 20, 38, and 38 in diameter with a stroke of 38 in. Speed 36 rev/min. Steam pressure 100 lb/in^2. Delivery 700 gallons of water per minute. Surface condenser. Length 46 ft 6 in, width 14 ft 0 in, height 9 ft 7 in.

(2) Cross compound with cylinders 21 and 36 in diameter by 27 in stroke, speed 48 rev/min. Steam pressure 100 lb/in^2, delivery 325 gallons per minute. Length 27 ft 3 in, width 10 ft 10 in, height 6 ft 10 in. Surface Condenser.

(3) Cross compound with cylinders 18 in and 32 in diameter, stroke 24 in. Speed 53 rev/min. Delivery 250 gallons per minute. Length 25 ft 6 in, width 9 ft 10 in, height 6 ft 6 in.

(4) Cross compound with cylinders 15½ in and 27 in diameter, stroke 22 in. Speed 57 rev/min. Delivery 170 gallons per minute. Length 24 ft 0 in, width 9 ft 2 in, height 5 ft 10 in.

A number of smaller twin high pressure cylinder engines were also offered. The delivery can be converted to horsepower bearing in mind that at an accumulator pressure of 750 lb/in^2, two gallons per minute equals one water horsepower.

Fig. 3.4 MODEL OF AN ARMSTRONG TYPE HYDRAULIC PUMPING ENGINE *c.* 1850.
(SCALE 1 : 8)
An earlier type had a plunger pump at each end of the steam cylinder but in the
model a single plunger pump is used with double connecting rods and two heavy
flywheels to even out the work over two strokes. Later the ram and piston pump
(Fig. 3.10 (f)) was used. The two domes connect with suction and delivery pipes
and contain strainers. Courtesy Science Museum.

In the first public hydraulic power station at Hull horizontal
engines were installed but in the London and later stations vertical
engines were used exclusively. For a given power output the
vertical engine, while requiring greater headroom, occupies only
half the floor space taken by the horizontal type. On the marine
side the vertical triple expansion engine with three cranks set at
120° to each other had been developed as a compact unit and the
general form of design was attractive for waterworks as well as
hydraulic supply stations. Initially the verticals were compounds
with two LP cylinders as shown in Fig. 3.5(a) and the partly
sectioned model Fig. 3.5(b), but later, to take advantage of the
economy of higher steam pressures, they were triple expansion.

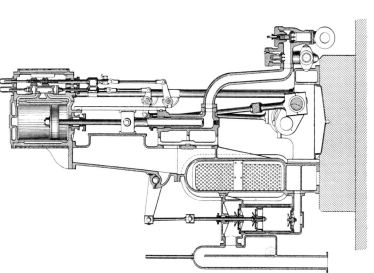

Fig. 3.5(a)   EARLY THREE CYLINDER COMPOUND PUMPING ENGINE. *(Proc. Instn Civ. Engrs 1887)*

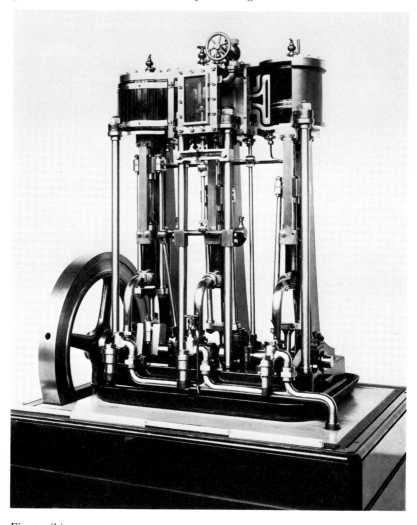

Fig. 3.5(b)   PARTLY SECTIONED MODEL OF A VERTICAL HYDRAULIC PUMPING ENGINE
1886. Made by the Hydraulic Engineering Co. (Scale 1 : 4)
The dimensions of the cylinders of the prototype were HP 19 in diameter, two LP
each 25 in diameter, stroke 24 in. Three plunger pumps 5 in diameter, 24 in
stroke. Duty 240 gallons per minute against a head of 750 lb/in² at 50 rev/min.
Later engines had three cylinders of increasing diameter giving triple expansion.
Courtesy Science Museum.

The use of three steam cylinders in conjunction with a three-throw crank with the cranks at 120° permitted the use of three directly driven single-acting ram pumps resulting in a well-balanced engine, together with a uniform delivery of water under pressure.

The finalized standard triple expansion unit made by the Hydraulic Engineering Co had an integral surface condenser and cylinders 15, 22, and 36 in diameter with a stroke of 24 in, speed 52 rev/min, steam pressure 150 lb/in^2, delivery 250 gallons per minute against an accumulator pressure of 800 lb/in^2. The three single-acting ram pumps driven direct by the piston rods were situated between the forks of the connecting rods (see Fig. 3.5). All the cylinders were steam jacketed, the jackets being formed by separate liners forced in, and the LP cylinder cover was also steam jacketed. The degree of expansion could be varied by means of expansion plates* on the back of the HP valve. The piston rods and pump rams were cottered into the crossheads, the rams being of gunmetal. The pump suction and delivery valves were conveniently located a little above the engine room floor. Engines were complete units with integral condensers and auxiliaries following the marine pattern. The floor space occupied by each set of engines was 14 ft 6 in by 11 ft 3 in, the height being 16 ft 3 in.

The earlier vertical compound surface condensing engines as shown in Fig. 3.5 had cylinders 19 in and 25 and 25 in with a stroke of 24 in, speed 52 rev/min, delivery 250 gallons per minute against an accumulator pressure of 800 lb/in^2, the steam pressure being 100 lb/in^2. The overall dimensions were 13 ft 6 in by 11 ft 2 in by 15 ft 6 in high.

---

* Admitting high-pressure steam behind an engine piston for the full length of the stroke gives the maximum power but is wasteful. Cutting off the supply of steam when the piston has only traversed part of its stroke results in less steam being used, and the expanding steam does work over the remainder of the stroke giving more work *per pound of steam*. The earlier the cut-off the greater the gain from expansive working. The simple slide valve can be designed to give a fixed cut-off but it has its limitations in this respect. Wide variation of the point of cut-off can be effected by means of an adjustable auxiliary valve, or 'expansion plates'. The main valve is modified and a separately operated adjustable valve slides on its back.

In effect an expansion valve is a means of obtaining the greatest possible degree of economy through expansive working, under varying conditions.

3.5 BOILERS

Cornish Boiler

This boiler was adopted by Trevithick when high-pressure steam was used in the Cornish engine. It can be considered as the first of a type of boiler known as the fire-tube or tank type boiler in contra-distinction to a later type, in which the tubes contained water, had little storage capacity, and was known as the water-tube type of boiler.

The Cornish boiler consisted of a large flat-ended cylindrical vessel, penetrated by one large 'fire-tube' containing the furnace, and mounted in brickwork in such a way that the products of combustion of the fuel heated as much as possible of the periphery of the outer cylinder (see Fig. 3.6). The hot gases from the burnt

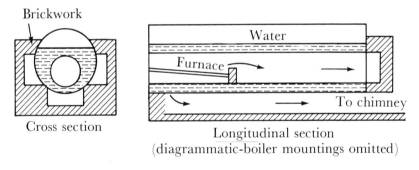

Brickwork

Cross section

Water

Furnace

To chimney

Longitudinal section
(diagrammatic-boiler mountings omitted)

Fig. 3.6   CORNISH BOILER

fuel pass over the brick bridge at the end of the grate to the end of the furnace tube where they are made to return through the side flues to the boiler front from which they again pass to the rear end along the bottom flue and thence up the chimney. Any sediment in the boiler water will collect at the bottom of the containing cylinder. By the time the products of combustion reach this portion they will have lost a lot of their heat and are thus not so likely to overheat the portion of the boiler where the sediment has collected.

Cornish boilers were in operation at the time but were not used in the hydraulic power stations. The boiler is mentioned here as the fore-runner of the popular Lancashire boiler.

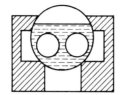

Fig. 3.7   CROSS SECTION OF LANCASHIRE BOILER

The Lancashire boiler

The Lancashire boiler (Fig. 3.7) has two furnace tubes instead of the one of the Cornish boiler and these were originally intended to be hand-fired alternately so that the combustion of smoke and unburnt gases from the freshly fired furnace would be assisted by the more intense heat from the bright fire of the other furnace.

The Lancashire boiler was probably the most popular of all the various stationary boilers and it was in common use in hydraulic power stations, the most common dimensions of the outer shell being 7 ft 6 in diameter by 28 ft long or 8 ft diameter by 30 ft long. Large powers could be catered for by using a battery of boilers.

In both Cornish and Lancashire boilers the heating surface was increased and the circulation of the water facilitated by the fitting of cross-tubes in the rear ends of the furnace tubes (Fig. 3.8). These cross-tubes, known as Galloway tubes, also acted as stays to the furnace tubes.

Although originally intended for hand firing the Lancashire

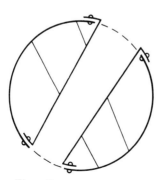

Fig. 3.8   GALLOWAY TUBES

boiler could be readily adapted for mechanical stoking and the Vicars' system was popular in hydraulic stations.

Vicars' Mechanical Stoker

Messrs T. & T. Vicars in 1867 and 1868 obtained patents for a method of mechanical stoking suitable for Lancashire and similar type boilers in which small coal was fed from a hopper and pushed into the furnace by means of two 'pushers' assisted by firebars having a longitudinal reciprocating motion.

Small coal and slack from the hopper passed into two boxes. From the boxes it was gradually pushed by reciprocating plungers acting alternately, into the furnace where it fell on to the firebars. The firebars had a slow reciprocating motion which gradually carried the burning mass to the rear. The clinker, ash, and any unburnt coal were ultimately discharged over the ends of the firebars into the flue where they formed a bank which acted as a bridge and closed the far end of the ashpit. Combustion of any of the fuel left was completed on this bank. The firebars, which were 2½ ft long, were followed by a perforated dead-plate 1 ft long, making the grate length 3½ ft. A bridge of brickwork was built in the flue 4 ft from the ends of the firebars. The travel of the firebars and the supply of fuel could each be varied independently. The variation in the travel of the firebars was from zero to 4 inches. Alternate firebars were automatically lowered and drawn towards the furnace front and then all the bars travelled forward together.

The Fairbairn–Beeley Boiler

Towards the end of the last century considerable attention was given to the development of the steam boiler particularly in the directions of the use of higher pressures, quicker steaming, increased size, and thermal efficiency, and it would take several volumes to outline the evolution of the boiler and to describe a fair selection of the boilers then available. One of direct interest is the Fairbairn–Beeley boiler. Figure 3.9 shows a sectional elevation and end view of this boiler without the brickwork. The burnt gases from the furnace (not shown) pass in the direction of the arrow through the small fire-tubes at the end of the furnace tube, return

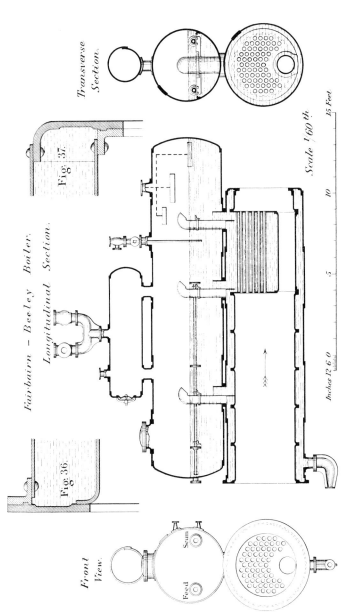

Transverse Section.

Scale ¹/60th.

Fig. 37.

Fairbairn – Beeley Boiler.

Longitudinal Section.

Fig. 36.

Inches 1' 6 0   5   10   15 Feet

Front View.

Scum

Feed

Fig. 3.9   FAIRBAIRN-BEELEY BOILER
(Proc. Instn Mech. Engrs 1895)

around the outside of the lower cylinder, pass to the upper one and then to the chimney.

Boilers of this type with a working pressure of 150 lb/in², were installed in the Wapping and City Road stations of the London Hydraulic Power Co. These boilers, fitted with economizers, on trial gave some outstanding results, it being reported that they were capable of evaporating 13·44 lb of water from and at 212°F per lb of coal having an evaporative power of 15·5 lb per lb thus giving a thermal efficiency of 86·7 per cent.

Economizers

The largest loss of heat in any boiler plant is that contained in the gases which pass up the chimney. Some loss is unavoidable since the gases will always be hotter than the water in the boiler. But the loss can be minimized by using some of the heat of the flue gases to heat the feed-water to the boiler. This is done by placing a series of pipes in the flue at the back of the boiler and passing the water through them on its way to the boiler. One of the most popular feed-water heaters was Green's Economizer which consisted of a nest of cast-iron pipes 4 in diameter by 10 ft long through which the feed-water was pumped in a direction opposite to the flow of the flue gases. The outer surfaces of the tubes were kept clean by scrapers which were made to travel slowly up and down the outside surfaces of the tubes.

3.6   CONDENSING PLANT

This consisted of the condenser, circulating pump, and air or extraction pump, these auxiliary pumps being driven through levers from the engine crosshead so that the whole formed a self-contained power unit. Today the tube condenser is in general use but is still referred to as the surface condenser to distinguish it from the now obsolete jet condenser. A surface condenser consists of a cast-iron vessel the ends of which are closed by two brass tube-plates between which are held a large number of brass tubes of ⅝ in or ¾ in diameter. The tubes are held by ferrules and packing in such a way that they are free to expand longitudinally. The circulating water is pumped through the tubes while the exhaust steam from the prime mover impinges on their external surfaces where it is condensed. The extractor pump extracts the condensate and maintains a vacuum in the condenser thus reducing the back pressure to a minimum.

3.7 PUMPS

There are three main types of pump, centrifugal, positive rotary, and reciprocating. The simple centrifugal pump consists of a runner in a casing which must be full of water. Rotation of the runner produces a forced vortex in the contained water resulting in an increase of pressure in a radial direction. The outward flow produces a partial vacuum at the centre of the runner and hence the necessary suction, resulting in water being forced up the suction pipe by atmospheric pressure, thus replacing that discharged outwards by the centrifugal action. In high lift pumps the required increase in pressure takes place in stages, an arrangement which is virtually a number of pumps in series.

The centrifugal pump is particularly suitable for running at the high rotational speeds developed by the steam turbine and the electric motor, and its even torque adds to its merits, so the development of both the steam turbine and the electric motor gave considerable impetus to the development of the centrifugal pump.

In the early years of the public hydraulic power stations, however, the centrifugal pump was only suitable for low heads, whereas the reciprocating pump had reached an advanced state of development and was particularly suited for use with the large slow-speed steam engines of the period. Tail-rod or cross-head drive made a very compact unit, while the heavy engine flywheel 'ironed out' variations in steam power output and pump demand, and at slow speeds and high heads it could attain very high efficiencies. The development of the turbine driven centrifugal pump came too late for it to have any serious influence on the fortunes of the public hydraulic power stations and there are only two isolated examples of the use of centrifugal pumps as supplementary equipment during developments in the later years of the era. Consequently, while noting that turbine and electrically driven centrifugal pumps were successfully used in later and larger dock hydraulic installations we have to consider them as somewhat outside the range of our story.

A positive pump is one in which once the fluid has been drawn into the pump it is bound to be forced out again. The reciprocating pump is a positive pump, the centrifugal is not. Many ingenious positive rotary pumps have been devised, and in general they are particularly suitable for electric drive. They have played a predominant part in the more recent developments in oil hydraulics and are likely to continue to play an important part in the future, but they again are outside the confines of our story. Consequently we shall here restrict our attention to reciprocating pumps.

The various types of reciprocating pump are shown diagrammatically in Fig. 3.10. All can operate vertically or horizontally with variation in layout, the simple outlines being adopted for clarity, though practical considerations may call for appreciable modification. Similarly, such details as packing and sealing arrangements, though of vital importance practically, have been omitted since our concern here is with basic principles.

The oldest and the simplest reciprocating pump is the bucket pump, Fig. 3.10(a). Raising the bucket creates a partial vacuum beneath it and the water is forced into the cylinder by the pressure of the atmosphere. On the downward stroke, return of the water is prevented by the foot valve and the water passes through the bucket to be lifted up to the delivery on the return stroke when the water flows out of the delivery pipe. Pumps which raise water by suction only are known as suction pumps. Their maximum lift is theoretically equal to the water barometer but in practice is about 25 ft (7·6 m). If it is desired to deliver the water under pressure a nonreturn valve can be put in the delivery pipe so that on the upward stroke water is forced through it. Delivery can be arranged to take place on the downward stroke by the arrangement of Fig. 3.10(b), which has the additional advantage of eliminating the valve in the bucket so that the bucket is replaced by a simple piston. For a given size of pump the quantity delivered can be almost doubled and a more even delivery obtained by making the pump doubleacting, i.e., it delivers on both the outward and return strokes. A horizontal double-acting pump is shown in Fig. 3.10(c).

When delivery at very high pressures is required, difficulties

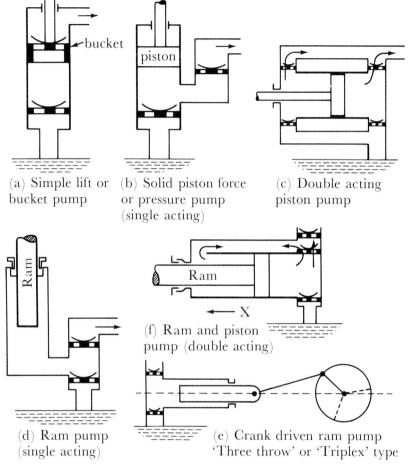

(a) Simple lift or bucket pump

(b) Solid piston force or pressure pump (single acting)

(c) Double acting piston pump

(f) Ram and piston pump (double acting)

(d) Ram pump (single acting)

(e) Crank driven ram pump 'Three throw' or 'Triplex' type

Fig. 3.10   RECIPROCATING PUMP TYPES

arise over leakage past piston and valves and the impossibility of being able to detect such leakage immediately. These difficulties can be minimized by the use of the ram pump, Fig. 3.10(d). Here all packing to prevent leakage is external and easily accessible. Suction takes place on the upward stroke and delivery by the downward displacement of the ram. The valves can be located where they are easily accessible. This was the type of pump used in the three-cylinder pumping units shown in Fig. 3.5 from which the accessibility of the pump glands and valves is obvious.

A single ram pump has the disadvantage of uneven delivery. In the three-cylinder steam pumping units the pump rams were connected to the engine cross-heads and since the engine cranks were at 120° to each other deliveries from the pumps were phased accordingly, giving a fairly even total delivery. A ram pump can also be driven by a crank and connecting rod Fig. 3.10(e) and when three ram pumps in line are driven by a three-throw crankshaft with cranks at 120° a similar effect is obtained, giving the three-throw ram, or triplex pump, a type which when driven by an electric motor through speed reduction gearing, played a prominent part in the electrification of some of the public hydraulic stations.

A double-acting ram and piston pump is shown in Fig. 3.10(f) and this type was commonly used in the early horizontal hydraulic pumping engines of the Armstrong type, Fig. 3.4, giving the advantage over the simple ram pump of a much more even delivery. In such a pump, if the area of the piston is A, the length of stroke L, and the cross-sectional area of the ram a, suction will take place when the piston moves in the direction shown by the arrow X while a volume $(A - a)L$ is delivered by the other side of the piston. But of the volume AL drawn in on the suction stroke, $(A - a)L$ will be passed to the other side of the piston on the return stroke, so the net delivery will be $AL - (A - a)L = aL$. It is advantageous to have the same volume delivered on each stroke, and for this to take place $(A - a)L$ must equal aL or $a = A/2$ that is, the cross-sectional area of the ram should be half that of the piston.

3.8   THE ACCUMULATOR

After leaving the pumps the pressure water passed to the accumulator or accumulators and from there into the mains for delivery to the consumers. Hydraulic accumulators are of two main types, those with a fixed vertical cylinder containing a loaded ram and those with a fixed vertical ram enclosed by a loaded cylinder. The first type was the earlier and the most common and is shown in Fig. 3.11.

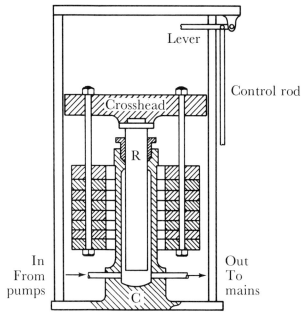

Fig. 3.11 HYDRAULIC ACCUMULATOR

The accumulator is a means of storing a relatively small amount of energy particularly useful in meeting suddenly fluctuating or intermittent demands, and serves to keep the pressure of supply constant, 'ironing out' the cyclical variation in pressure from the pumps. It is not a means of storing large amounts of energy.

In Fig. 3.11, C is the cylinder fed with pressure water from the pumps through the supply pipe, and R is the ram fitted at its top with a cross-head, which is guided as it moves upward by shoes sliding on ways attached to vertical columns. From this cross-head are suspended weights which load the ram to give the required working pressure which will be the total weight on the ram divided by the cross-sectional area of the ram. The ram can be loaded by cast-iron weights but in the larger sizes these are replaced by a container which can be loaded with scrap metal, concrete or stones, etc.

One or more accumulators would be installed at each hydraulic power station and accumulators could be sited at strategic points along the supply main housed in suitable sub-stations. Main station accumulators could be fitted with controlling gear, a simple form being the lever system shown in Fig. 3.11 in which the lever is pushed up by the ram cross-head on reaching its highest point of travel. The movement could be used to operate pump control gear or the throttle valve of a steam engine.

Where the use of unnecessarily heavy equipment is out of the question, e.g., aboard ship, the ram weight of an accumulator can be replaced by a large piston, working in a cylinder to which steam is admitted. If the steam supply to the pumping engine is taken through this cylinder the ram piston can be made to open or close steam ports thus automatically controlling the speed of the pumping engine to match the demand. Steam-operated hydraulic accumulators have been used in connection with gunnery equipment but were not in use in the public hydraulic stations.

3.9   OUTPUT CONTROL AND MEASUREMENT OF WATER USED

The station output of pressure water depended on the number of engines in operation and engine speed, and, of course, had to meet the demand, the variation in which was indicated by the rise or fall of the accumulator ram which could be used as a means of automatic or semi-automatic control of engine speed.

Two most important measurements required in assessing the efficiency of a station are the power delivered into the mains by the pumping engines and the rate of flow throughout the day. The daily check on engine power was obtained from the number of engine revolutions as determined from counters. This was multiplied by a constant which for the London stations was 4·8 gallons per revolution. The value of the constant was periodically checked by direct measurement of the quantity used over several hours from the supply tanks. The meters installed in consumers' premises were read every six or seven weeks and from these readings the overall efficiency of the system could be expressed as the ratio of the total quantity registered by the meters to the quantity determined from the engine counters. This figure was quoted by Ellington in 1895 for the London system as varying from 0·9826 to

0·8560, the figure varying in different quarters and in different years.

The discrepancy between the quantity delivered, as estimated from engine counter readings, and the total quantity as indicated by customers' meters, was due to waste and error, and the sources of these could be divided into two classes, those which occurred before the consumers' premises were reached and those which occurred on the consumers' premises, i.e, those connected with the consumers' machinery and meters.

The first included pump, mains, and general delivery losses, i.e., leakage past suction valves, glands, etc., leakage in the mains, and the loss involved in pumping to waste to maintain circulation during frosty weather. The second was due to faulty meters and leakage from customers' machines since, for reasons given later, it was the practice to measure the exhaust water, and there was also a somewhat large loss due to the practice of consumers draining their pipes at the end of the day. To determine the minimum rate of flow, i.e., the rate of flow when it could be assumed that no work was being done, and to obtain more information on losses, automatic flow recorders were used. In these a drum was driven by a clock mechanism, the drum carrying a paper strip marked with quarter-hour divisions. Above the drum were a number of armatures each connected electrically to an engine. The armatures carried pins which pricked the paper as each engine completed 100 revolutions. Where a number of stations were involved the clock mechanisms were synchronized. The maximum delivery was used to determine the load factor while the minimum delivery indicated the general condition of the whole system.

Consumers' Meters
The ideal solution here would have been high-pressure meters situated at the point of entry of the supply so that all the installation beyond the meter was the responsibility of the consumer. But high-pressure meters to stand pressures of 700 to 1200 lb/in², were very expensive and it was generally felt that meters should be positive, that is they should directly measure the quantity used (as distinct from inferential meters which register related factors such as drop in pressure on passage through an orifice, from which the

quantity flowing can be inferred, or the speed of a small turbine which is proportional to the rate of flow). But positive meters, however desirable, have disadvantages. They offer considerable resistance to flow at high velocities and if they get out of order they may seriously restrict or stop the flow entirely.

After all the factors had been considered the general choice was, wherever possible, to use low-pressure meters measuring the discharge from a tank into which the consumer's machinery exhausted. The meter finally adopted was the Parkinson, Fig. 3.12, which resembles to some extent a standard gas meter. Should it stop working the tank collecting the exhaust water would overflow thus drawing immediate attention to the fault.

In the Parkinson meter, water from the inlet pipe passes into the float chamber (back view, Fig. 3.11) the level in which is maintained uniform by means of a float and valve. The water leaves the float chamber through the bend (see longitudinal section) and flows into the annular space of a hollow revolving drum. The drum interior is divided into four compartments formed by oblique radiating plates, each compartment being able in turn to receive

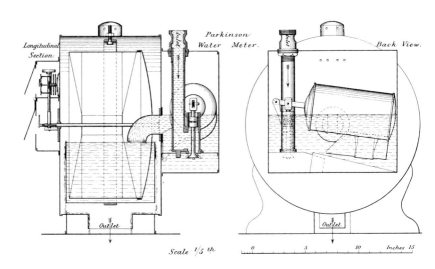

Fig. 3.12   PARKINSON WATER METER
(*Proc. Instn Mech. Engrs* 1895)

water from the annular space. As each compartment fills the weight of the water in it causes the drum to rotate, thus bringing the next compartment into communication with the water in the annular space. At the same time the outlet from the first compartment, on the opposite side of the drum, falls below the level of the water in that compartment, so that the water flows away into the trough in which the drum rotates, and from there into the discharge pipe. The height of the trough is adjustable. The discharge per revolution from the drum will depend upon the depth to which the drum is immersed in the trough and hence the discharge per revolution can be adjusted. The volume of water passing can be registered by a suitable counting mechanism.

Cases did arise where it was only possible to measure the flow on the high-pressure side of an installation. An example was London docks where only a portion of the demand was met by the London Hydraulic Power Co, the remainder of the power required being supplied by the dock pumping stations. A meter used in such cases was the Kent Water Meter, Fig. 3.13. This meter is virtually a simple rotary piston engine in which a hollow elliptical vulcanite piston is rotated in a chamber by the pressure water, the piston rotating and sliding freely on a hub which is eccentric to the working chamber. The piston has a central pin which describes a circular path and operates the counting mechanism. Leakage losses could increase with wear so wear of the piston is compensated for by an adjustable metal tongue shown below the piston in the plan view of Fig. 3.13. When the piston is in the position shown dotted in the plan, water entering through the inlet port will flow in the direction of the arrows shown on the left-hand side of the vertical section, and will press on the left side of the piston, causing it to rotate clockwise until the water can escape through the port on the right of the section, and then to the outlet, as shown by the arrows. By then the other side of the piston will be exposed to the incoming water and the process will be repeated. The principal difficulties with high-pressure meters centre around the counter mechanism. The spindle must be light to avoid undue loss of pressure and the stuffing box must be kept tight under the ensuing wear.

Meters of the Kent type do not register small flows accurately

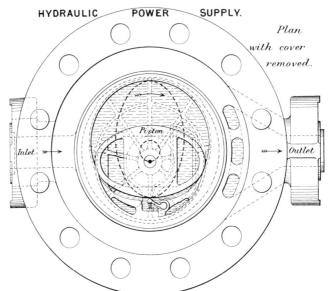

HYDRAULIC   POWER   SUPPLY.

*Plan
with cover
removed.*

Piston

Inlet   *Outlet*

Kent   Water   Meter.

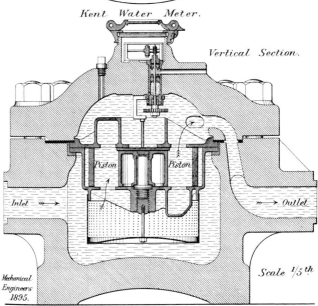

Vertical Section.

Piston   *Piston*

Inlet   *Outlet*

*Mechanical
Engineers
1895.*

Scale 1/5 th

Fig. 3.13   KENT WATER METER

but they take up very little space and there is no noise from falling
water. Meters of the Parkinson type, on the other hand, will
measure small flows very accurately provided the water is clean,
but they take up much more room. Also should dirt or rubbish pass
into the drum as is much more likely when measurements are made
on the exhaust side of an installation, the accuracy of the meter is
soon affected and the meter has to be replaced. Some trouble was
experienced in this direction when machinery was badly maintained, poor packing used, or rams and glands were in bad
condition.

.10 CONSUMERS' EQUIPMENT

Public hydraulic power stations supplied power in competition
with gas, steam, electricity, and to a limited extent compressed air,
and were well able to hold their own especially where the demand
was intermittent. None of the systems was designed as a means of
continuously supplying power other than in the special case of
Antwerp where the system was laid out specifically as a special
means of distributing power for the generation of electricity for
lighting, but at a number of places in London hydraulic power was
used to generate electricity on site at a price competitive with that
of the local electricity station. A very suitable power unit for this
purpose was the Pelton wheel which on account of its high rotational speed could be directly coupled to a dynamo, and generating
sets consisting of a Pelton wheel directly coupled to a dynamo were
available as standard units. Rotative power was required for a
number of other purposes, some involving variable speed and some
relatively slow speed operation, and to meet these requirements a
number of hydraulic engines of the ram type were available. The
efficiency of the Pelton wheel falls under variable load and to use it
for the operation of slow speed machinery involves the use of
gearing.

Lifts and hoists
Lifts and hoists were the most popular applications of hydraulic
power. The simplest form is virtually a hydraulic jack with a
platform mounted on top of the ram, the platform being guided in

its vertical motion by slideways. The ram cylinder will need to be sunk in the ground and to be of a length somewhat in excess of the total lift, i.e., the lift when the ram is at the end of its outward travel. Suitable control gear will be necessary to operate valves admitting water to the cylinder and releasing water from it. Such a simple arrangement is ideal for comparatively low lifts such as with goods hoists and a simple case is the modern car hoist in common use in garages. The system, however, has a number of drawbacks which render it unsuitable where the height of lift is appreciable.

For appreciable lifts the ram cylinder has to be correspondingly long and must be housed in a borehole which in itself could be an expensive proposition. Also the ram must support the lift cage and its contents and when fully extended it is a long column which must have sufficient cross-sectional area to avoid buckling. The lifting force will be the pressure of the water multiplied by the cross-sectional area of the ram and if this area is large (to avoid buckling) the pressure may need to be correspondingly low. Should water be supplied at the normal pressure of 700 lb/in^2 some form of pressure reducing equipment may be called for.

On the upstroke the total load on the ram will be that due to the weight of the ram, the weight of the cage, the net load, the force necessary to overcome friction (in glands, etc.) and the accelerating force. The lift ram will be immersed in the water in its own cylinder and consequently, as a floating body, will be subject to an upthrust equal to the weight of water it displaces. This upthrust will decrease as the ram moves upwards, that is the effective weight of the ram will increase as it moves upwards. If R_B = ram weight at the bottom of its stroke, C = cage weight, and L = net load lifted, then the total load on the ram at the commencement of its upward stroke = $[R_B + C + L +$ (force to overcome friction) + (force to accelerate the total moving mass)]. For preliminary calculation purposes the force to overcome friction and the accelerating force were usually lumped together and taken as 25 per cent of the gross load, i.e., (weight of ram + cage + net load) and denoted by F.

On the return stroke from the topmost position of the cage the effective weight of the ram will now have increased by an amount equal to the weight of water displaced by it when at the bottom of its stroke so the load on the ram at the commencement of the downward stroke will be $(R_T + C + F)$ where $R_B - R_T$ = weight of water displaced by ram throughout its travel. Some excess force is necessary to drive the water out of the ram cylinder on the return stroke.

There is a considerable amount of work wasted in pushing up the cage and ram and allowing them to return each time, and this can be avoided by counterbalancing the cage and ram. Counterbalancing can be done by a counterpoise chain and weights, the chain passing over a pulley at the head of the lift shaft and hanging freely, together with any balance weights, between the cage guides. Alternatively the cage and ram can be counterbalanced hydraulically and a number of ingenious hydraulic balances were devised. A simple example illustrative of the common principle is shown diagrammatically in Fig. 3.14. This balance has two external water supplies, one from the pressure mains and the other an auxiliary supply of low pressure from a tank situated in any convenient position. It will be assumed that the lift has been designed or that it is required to fit the balance to an existing lift. Then the total displacement of the lift ram, the working pressure, and the weights of the cage and the ram will be known.

The upper or balance cylinder (Fig. 3.14) contains a piston while the lower or load cylinder also contains a piston, the two pistons being connected together by a rod. Beneath the balance piston is an annular chamber (3) which receives water from the lift cylinder as the lift ram descends and supplies water under pressure when the lift ram is required to ascend, so its maximum volume has to be slightly in excess of the total displacement of the lift ram.

It is possible to obtain the *ratios* between the areas of the pistons to obtain any degree of balance, and hence the design proportions of the hydraulic balance, by first assuming the annular area of the underside of the balance piston to have the unit value a_3 equal to the cross-sectional area of the lift ram.

The water from the low pressure (tank) system, at a pressure p_1 is made to press on the top of the balance piston to supply the balancing force, so if a_1 is the unit area of the piston top, $p_1 a_1 = R_B + C$.

Water at mains pressure, denoted by p_2 is admitted to the annular space above the piston in the load cylinder to supply the

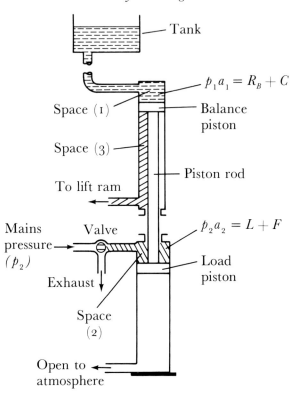

Fig. 3.14   SIMPLE HYDRAULIC BALANCE FOR LIFTS

force necessary to lift the load and overcome friction, and supply the necessary acceleration. So if a_2 is the unit annular area of the top of the load piston, $p_2\,a_2 = L + F$.

Starting with the lift ram at the bottom of its stroke, the balance and load pistons will be at the top of their travel. Low pressure water will constantly be admitted above the balance piston. If now mains water is admitted above the load piston there will result a total downward unit load of $R_B + C + L + F$ applied to the water in the annular chamber (3), generating therein sufficient pressure which when transmitted to the lift ram will cause it to rise (since $a_3 = $ cross-sectional area of ram). As the ram and the lift cage move upwards the effective weight of the lift ram increases. But the

balance and load pistons move downwards so there is an increasing head of water above both and the extra load due to this
increasing head will serve to increase the pressure in the annular
chamber beneath the balance piston and hence the pressure
beneath the lift ram.

When the valve admitting water above the load piston is closed
the lift comes to rest. When this valve is opened to exhaust the lift
starts to descend. As the lift ram falls water is returned to the
annular chamber (3) and the balance piston moves upwards
forcing the low pressure water above it to return to the tank. On
descending the lift ram loses effective weight but at the same time
the head of water above the balance and load pistons decreases so

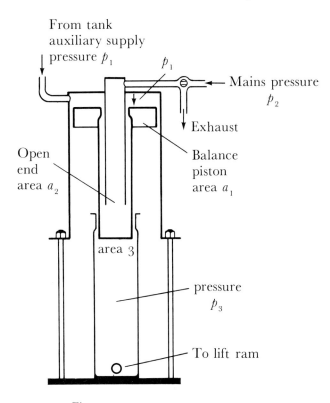

Fig. 3.15   ALTERNATIVE LIFT BALANCE

balance is maintained. The space below the load piston is left open to the atmosphere.

In the foregoing calculations the whole of the weight of the ram and cage has been balanced but obviously the calculations can be modified to balance any required fraction of this weight and some unbalanced weight will ensure a more rapid descent of the cage if so desired. The calculations give the ratios $a_1 : a_2 : a_3$. Exact sizes can be determined to suit individual cases, e.g., if a_3 is made double the cross-sectional area of the lift ram the other areas are increased proportionally, the design sizes being determined to suit supply conditions.

An alternative form of balance is shown in Fig. 3.15. Here the mains pressure water is admitted via the central pipe to a hollow ram. The annular balance piston is subjected to a pressure p_1 from the auxiliary tank supply. The total load on the end of the ram supplies the balancing and lifting forces creating the pressure p_3 in the cylinder from which the water to operate the lift is supplied. A lift with hydraulic balance is shown in Fig. 3.16.

As a further alternative the auxiliary water supply (Fig. 3.15) can be dispensed with and the annular balance piston loaded by means of a suitable hanger with weights sufficient to provide the required degree of balancing. In this case the variation in the effective weight of the lift ram is not provided for but this is often a small quantity compared with the other loads involved.

Multiple Chain or Wire Rope Lifts

A direct-acting ram lift could be a relatively costly job owing to the fact that a long ram cylinder is required and this has to be housed in a suitable borehole. An alternative to having a ram with a very long stroke is to use a short stroke ram with multiplying gear. One form of multiplying gear was virtually the common pulley block system in reverse. In the simple system of pulley blocks, Fig. 3.17(a), if the number of rope lengths between the blocks is n (equal to the total number of pulleys, six in this case) then the effort end of the rope E will move n times the distance the weight W is lifted, and the distance the weight is lifted is the decrease in the distance between the blocks. Putting this in reverse, if we force the blocks apart a distance x then the effort end will move

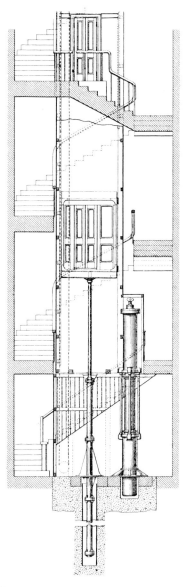

Fig. 3.16 HYDRAULIC BALANCE PASSENGER LIFT 1887

(*Proc. Instn Civ. Engrs* 1887)

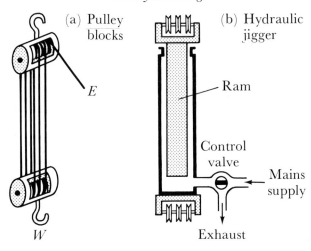

Fig. 3.17   HYDRAULIC JIGGER

a distance nx. This is the principle of the hydraulic multiplier known as the 'Jigger' in which the hemp ropes of the pulley blocks are replaced by strong chains or wire ropes, moving over smooth grooved pulleys, and the sets of pulleys are pushed apart by a short stroke ram as shown in Fig. 3.17(b) with the chains or ropes removed for clarity. One end of the chain is anchored to the jigger while the free end is used for lifting or pulling purposes. When used for lift operation the jigger can be placed in any convenient position, consideration of course being given to accessibility for maintenance purposes. The free end of the chain or rope passed over a pulley at the top of the lift shaft, the cage being suspended from it. Stops were provided to prevent the jigger over-stroking.

A number of variations of the jigger-operated lift were available with different methods of balancing and various provisions such as safety catches, etc., were necessary but all these are matters of lift design and will be found adequately dealt with in books on that subject. Here we are concerned with the basic principles of the main applications of hydraulic power.

In the outline diagrams given, the lift operating valves are shown circular in form for simplicity, but in practice they were of the slide type. In one form a rack on the back of the slide valve meshed with a pinion to the shaft of which was keyed a large rope wheel which could be operated by a rope or wire cable. Suitable ports in the body of the valve communicated with the supply, the lift operating mechanism, or waste.

Jiggers were not only used for lift operation. They could be applied to all kinds of existing cranes and hoists and they became very popular with warehouse owners and wharfingers in replacing hand or steam operation when public hydraulic supplies became available. They had the advantages that they could be placed in almost any position, maintenance was minimal, skilled operators were not required, and remote control was possible. Their main disadvantage was the relatively low overall efficiency. Gibson* quotes the value of the efficiency of a well-designed jigger having large pulleys with wire ropes, well lubricated, as:

efficiency $= 0.86 - 0.02\ n$, n being the number of multiplications of the stroke.

Cranes

For crane operation hydraulic power offered, and still offers, a number of advantages such as convenience, safety, steadiness in operation, and adaptability to meet a range of varying conditions, being more suitable in one or more of these respects than its competitors steam, compressed air, and electricity. The basic operating mechanism is the jigger, separate ones usually being employed for the operations of lifting, racking, and slewing.

In the case of the simple jigger the same amount of water is used per stroke whether the load is a light or a heavy one. When it is required to cope with a wide range of loads consideration has to be given to economy in the use of power water when dealing with the lighter loads. With this in mind a telescopic ram may be used, the larger ram providing the working chamber for the smaller one while itself working in a pressure chamber (Fig. 3.18). For heavy loads the two rams work together as one. When dealing with lighter loads the larger ram is locked in position, when the smaller one copes with the load.

Possibly the simplest form of hydraulic crane and one widely in

* *Hydraulics And Its Applications* by A. H. Gibson, Constable & Co, 1925, p. 737.

The Hydraulic Age

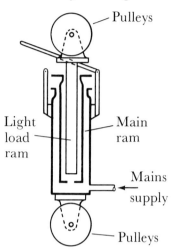

Fig. 3.18 DIAGRAMMATIC OUTLINE OF TWO POWER CRANE JIGGER (TELESCOPIC RAM)

use where public hydraulic supplies were available is the wall type warehouse crane shown in Fig. 3.19 which was in common use for off-loading in warehouses. The operating jigger was mounted on the wall and the operating gear placed in any suitable position. This would usually consist of a slide valve operated by a rope or levers.

The fixed wharf crane was one of the earliest types of crane and due to its simplicity and suitability the general design remained unchanged for many years. The pillar was housed in a pit and rested upon a footplate. The pillar top carried a bearing ring permitting it to revolve in a bedplate fixed just below ground level. Around the pillar bearing ring was a chainwheel built in segments for ease of assembly. On each side was placed a cylinder and ram with a chain passing from one ramhead round the chainwheel to the other ramhead opposite. On pressure being admitted to one cylinder the ram would move out pulling the chain and thus causing the crane to swing around and at the same time pulling back the ram of the opposite cylinder so forcing out to exhaust the water it contained. The controlling mechanism would be a slide valve capable of admitting water to one cylinder while placing the opposite one in communication with the exhaust. A valve for each

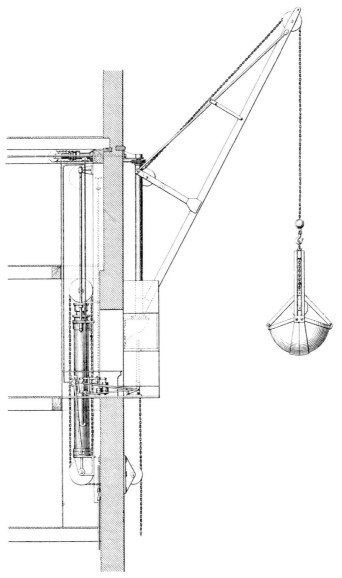

Fig. 3.19 HYDRAULIC WALL CRANE
(*Proc. Instn Civ. Engrs* 1887)

cylinder would be required with independent hand manipulating levers. Surmounting the crane post were two side frames enclosing the lifting jigger from which a chain passed up and over the pulley at the top of the crane jib to the crane hook. The top of the jib was stayed to the top of the side frames.

Fixed wharf cranes had the disadvantage of lack of mobility. Modern wharf cranes are arranged to travel on rails along the wharf with a hydraulic pressure main along the line of the rails and hydrants at regular intervals, the water being conveyed from these by telescopic and swivelling pipes. In the case of large cranes the gauge of the track may be much greater than the standard railway gauge and the central portion of the lower part of the crane casing may be cut away to enable railway trucks or vehicles to pass under the crane.

Hydraulic cranes today are made in a wide range of sizes and their applications are numerous, but the basic working principle remains that of the hydraulic jigger.

Presses

The hydraulic press is the oldest of the hydraulic tools and at the same time the most versatile. Bramah in 1795 was granted a patent for a hydraulic press which was driven by a hand-operated pump. As the virtues of the press became appreciated it was adapted for such work as baling or packing, and seed crushing. Early baling presses were hand operated and consisted of a table or platen pushed upwards towards a head supported by four circular columns. The underface of the head and the top face of the platen had a number of grooves machined in them to permit of the insertion of bands or hoops for the fastening of the bale after it had been compressed. The base of the press would consist of a cistern with two pumps, a larger diameter pump for supplying a relatively high quantity of water at a low pressure for the first part of the stroke of the press, and the smaller diameter pump to supply the high pressure necessary for the final squeeze, a safety valve being provided to prevent undue pressure being exerted on the bale.

The following are the main details and dimensions of a typical early baling press and serve to indicate the type of instrument and its capabilities. Hand lever three feet long from point of application of load to fulcrum and two inches from fulcrum to centre-line of pump plunger, giving a leverage of 18 to 1. Pump plunger ¾ in diameter, cross-sectional area 0·44 in². Taking the load on the hand lever as 50 lb, load on pump plunger = 18 × 50 lb. Pressure developed by pump = 900/0·44 = 2045 lb/in².

The ram of the press is 12 in diameter and hence has a cross-sectional area of 113 in². Load exerted by press = 113 × 2045 = 231 085 lb. This will be reduced slightly by packing friction. Such a press then would be capable of a final squeeze of a full hundred tons.

For the initial stage of compression a pump with a plunger diameter of 1½ in would be used. This would give four times the delivery per stroke at a quarter of the pressure, i.e., a more rapid initial compression at a pressure of approximately 500 lb/in², the consequent reduction in pumping time being of particular importance in the case of hand operation.

For such a press the distance between the under side of the head and the platen in its lowest position would be 4 ft 6 in, and the stroke of the ram 3 ft. It should be noted that a reduction in the working pressure could result in an unduly large ram to obtain the same final squeeze.

With the coming of the public hydraulic power stations presses could be operated from the hydraulic mains. The pressure of 700 to 800 lb/in² was, however, low for their operation and for some purposes, e.g., the final squeeze in baling, some means of increasing the operating pressure, such as an intensifier, would be necessary. The stations at Glasgow and Manchester operated at pressures in the region of half a ton per square inch mainly because of the fact that there was a heavy demand for power for presses used for baling in both these areas.

With the demise of the stations not only did the press survive but it entered a new era of prosperity. With electro-hydraulic unit rotary pumps operating with oil as the working fluid the press today is a most versatile piece of plant, presses being used for a wide variety of manufacturing processes, e.g., hot-forming or forging, coldforming, plastics manufacture, deep drawing, boiler drum and pipe forming, straightening, sintering, etc., and various types of hydraulic testing machines are virtually calibrated presses.

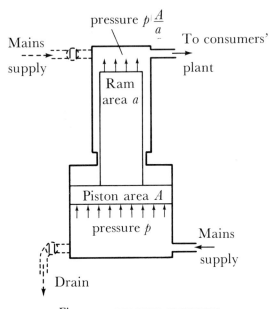

Fig. 3.20   PRESSURE INTENSIFIER
(Dotted lines show additions for repeated operation)

Intensifiers

When the mains pressure is lower than that required an intensifier
had to be used. In principle an intensifier consists of a piston of
area A to which is attached a ram of lesser area a (Fig. 3.20). Mains
water of pressure p is admitted behind the piston so that the
resulting upward force is pA. Hence the pressure by the ram pA/a.
That is, neglecting friction, the mains pressure is increased in
intensity in the ratio A/a.

With this arrangement water is only delivered to the plant on the
upward stroke of the ram. To obtain a further supply at the higher
pressure it is necessary, by a suitable arrangement of valves, to
draw away the water from beneath the piston and admit mains
water to the ram cylinder. The piston will then descend and the
operation can be repeated . The supply obtained in this way will be
intermittent. To obtain a continuous supply two intensifiers are required, one operating the valves of the other so that one is
delivering while the other is recharging.

When a press is being operated the water from below the piston, instead of being drained to waste, can be used to raise the press platen and perform the initial squeeze.

Hydraulic Engines

Hydraulic engines convert the reciprocating motion of the ram into rotary motion. Many ideas were put forward in this direction but we shall only mention here a few that met with practical success and were well-known. Possibly the simplest and most well known was the Ramsbottom engine which had three rams working in three oscillating cylinders (Fig. 3.21). The engine was built within a vertical rectangular frame. Each cylinder oscillated independently upon a hollow trunnion situated at the bottom of the frame. This hollow trunnion was divided into two parts by a longitudinal partition, one side serving as the inlet or delivery main and the other as the exhaust or discharge main, and it had exhaust and delivery ports cut in it to serve each cylinder. Each ram was attached directly to a three-throw crankshaft at the top of the frame. The water entered by a flanged branch piece at the base of the frame and passed into the delivery side of the hollow trunnion.

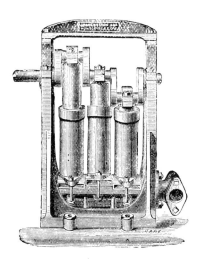

Fig. 3.21   RAMSBOTTOM HYDRAULIC ENGINE

As each cylinder oscillated a port at its base coincided alternately with the delivery and exhaust ports in the trunnion. The exhaust water was carried away by a flanged connection on the opposite side of the frame.

The radial oscillating cylinder engine had three cylinders in the same plane, set at 120° to each other. The rams acted on a common crankpin of a central crankshaft. The cylinders had ball ends each containing a port which alternately registered with admission and exhaust ports in the frame. Advantages of the oscillating cylinder engine were that the usual separate piston- and connecting-rods were dispensed with and by the use of a suitable change-over valve exhaust ports could become delivery ports and vice versa, and so the engine could be quickly and easily reversed. A disadvantage of such an engine when used on a hydraulic system was that the cylinder capacity was fixed, that is the same amount of water was

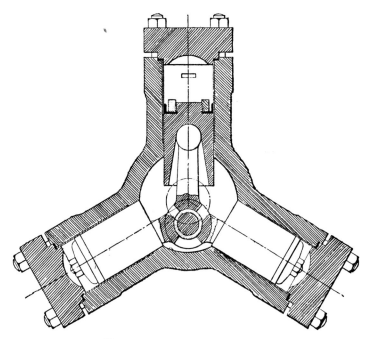

Fig. 3.22 BROTHERHOOD ENGINE
Admission of water to the cylinders is controlled by a rotary valve not shown.

required per revolution whether the engine was lightly or heavily loaded.

Another radial engine was the Brotherhood engine (Fig. 3.22) in which the three cylinders, set at 120° to each other, were fixed, being integral in one casting while the plungers were virtually pistons with orthodox type connecting rods. The water was admitted to, and exhausted from, each cylinder by means of a rotary valve. The Brotherhood engine was extensively used for such work as the operation of capstans, being built in sizes up to 30 h.p. with a piston speed of 30 ft/min, and capable of working with water pressures from 60 lb/in² upwards. The Brotherhood engine suffered from the same drawback as oscillating cylinder engines, that is the drawback of all fixed stroke hydraulic engines. Owing to the fact that water, unlike air and steam, cannot be used expansively, at the same speed the same quantity of water, and hence the same energy, is required regardless of the load on the engine.

A number of attempts were made to overcome this drawback and a number of variable power engines resulted. The most successful was the Rigg engine, shown in Fig. 3.23, in which a flywheel was mounted on the main driving shaft. The ring of the flywheel carried three equi-distant crankpins to each of which was connected a plunger working in a hydraulic cylinder. The three cylinders were integral with a ring which revolved freely around a hollow shaft set in front of the flywheel, the centre of the hollow shaft being eccentric to the centre of the main shaft so that the cylinders revolved about a centre while the associated plungers revolved about a centre eccentric to it, thus producing relative reciprocating motion between plunger and cylinder, the stroke of which was double the eccentricity. The eccentricity could be varied by moving the centre about which the cylinders revolved. When the centres of rotation coincided, i.e., the eccentricity was zero, the stroke was zero. Then the engine could be reversed by moving the pin to one side or the other of the central position. In small engines the centre could be moved by means of a handwheel and screw, but in larger sizes a hydraulic relay was used. This relay in effect consisted of two rams of different diameters working in opposition to each other and carrying between them a slide holding the movable centre on which the cylinders revolved. The constant

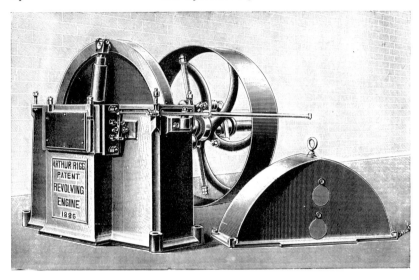

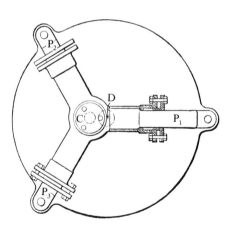

Fig. 3.23   RIGG HYDRAULIC ENGINE

Pistons P_1, P_2, P_3 are pinned to a disc which revolves around a fixed centre D. The three cylinders rotate about a centre C which can be moved closer to or farther away from the disc centre and the stroke is twice CD, the distance between the disc and cylinder centres.

mains pressure was applied to the smaller ram but the admission and exhaust of pressure water to the larger ram were controlled by valves which moved with the ram and the slide so that they closed themselves. Pressure applied to the larger ram would cause it to move against the smaller one and carry the bearing pin with it, but the opening of the exhaust valve would reduce the pressure behind the larger ram allowing the mains pressure on the smaller ram to move the bearing pin in the opposite direction. When both admission and exhaust valves were closed the bearing pin was securely held.

A governor could be fitted which acting upon the valves would serve to keep the speed constant within limits under varying loads.

The hollow shaft on which the cylinders revolved served as the supply pipe, the distribution of water being by means of ports in the side of the central boss of the cylinder block, and as the cylinders revolved their ports successively opened to inlet and exhaust.

Pumping Applications

Pumping applications included not only the use of hydraulic pumps for the pumping of water and other liquids, but cellar draining pumps, hydraulic hydrants, and fire-fighting systems in which the pressure of the domestic water mains was increased by the use of hydraulic injectors in order to throw a jet to the top of the highest buildings. Hydraulically operated domestic vacuum cleaners were also available.

The basic principle of such devices was that of the hydraulic jet pump, the mode of operation of which will be described next.

The hydraulic jet pump

Water under pressure possesses energy. If the water is allowed to escape through a hole into the atmosphere its pressure will fall but the decrease in pressure energy will appear as velocity energy. The sum total of its energy will remain constant, that is, as its pressure energy decreases its velocity energy increases and vice versa. This can be shown experimentally. Figure 3.24 depicts the flow of water in a convergent–divergent pipe which at all times is running full. In the convergent portion between A and B the cross-sectional area is decreasing and since the quantity passing will be the same at all

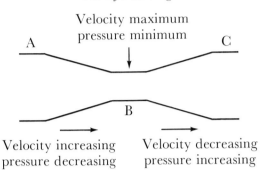

Fig. 3.24   CONVERGENT – DIVERGENT FLOW

sections of the pipe, the velocity in this portion must steadily increase. The velocity at B will be much greater than that at A and the insertion of a pressure gauge at B will show that the pressure is correspondingly less. In the divergent portion from B to C the velocity decreases and the pressure builds up until at C the pressure is almost the same as at A (the slight difference will be the small frictional loss).

This principle is made use of in the jet pump. Pressure water is made to issue from a comparatively small jet so that the velocity of the water is very high and consequently its pressure at the point of exit is low. The low pressure in the region of the jet mouth can be used to draw in water, air, or other fluid through a suction pipe (Fig. 3.25). The fluid drawn in will mix with the water from the jet and the combined fluid will go forward to a divergent portion of the pump body in which its velocity will be reduced and a pressure

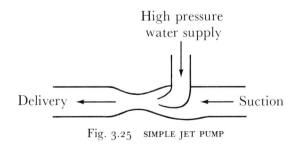

Fig. 3.25   SIMPLE JET PUMP

built up in the delivery pipe. This delivery pressure will be less than that of the mains supply but higher than that of the suction fluid. The delivery pressure can be varied by adjusting the proportion of high-pressure to low-pressure fluid.

In this way a small quantity of high-pressure water from a hydraulic main could be used to feed a large quantity of low-pressure water into a delivery pipe at a pressure lower than that of the hydraulic supply, but greater than that of the low-pressure supply.

It must be noted that in pipe flow any change of velocity must be gradual. A sudden change in velocity results in shock, the formation of eddies (turbulence), and consequent energy loss.

There is appreciable impact between the two streams of fluid in a jet pump and the loss of energy due to shock and eddy formation is significant. Consequently the jet pump is not an efficient means of pumping but it is very convenient and simple, and for many purposes these considerations outweigh its lack of efficiency.

Fire Hydrants
Fire fighting is an example of the utilization of the jet pump where its low efficiency is more than compensated for by its simplicity, convenience, and low first cost. The loss of energy due to shock can be reduced, and hence the efficiency of the pump increased, by performing the operation in two or more stages, and this method was adopted by Greathead in his injector hydrant (Fig. 3.26). By itself water at high pressure from the hydraulic power mains could not be supplied in adequate quantity to have an effect on a large fire and though an adequate quantity may be available from the domestic supply mains the pressure may not be sufficient to force the water to the height of the nearest building. Where the two mains were close together it was possible to use an injector hydrant to increase the pressure of the jet from the low-pressure mains thus providing a jet capable of reaching to the required height with the use of comparatively little high-pressure water, and what was used supplemented the volume of the water in the delivery pipe. A number of such hydrants were installed by Hull Corporation following the line of the hydraulic company's main in High Street and they proved particularly valuable in fighting several ware-

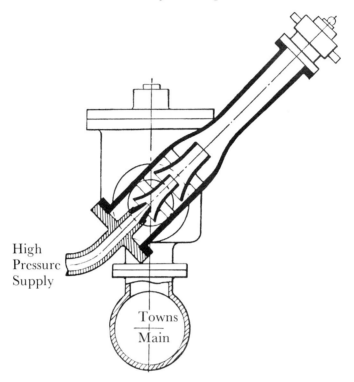

High
Pressure
Supply

Towns
Main

Fig. 3.26   GREATHEAD FIRE HYDRANT
The velocity of the low-pressure water is increased in stages

house fires in that area. Owners of premises who installed such an appliance were allowed preferential insurance rates.

Sprinkler Systems
Sprinkler fire-fighting systems were also operated by hydraulic injectors. Here it was necessary to have an automatic control so that the hydraulic power supply was cut off except when the sprinkler system was operating. This was effected by a ram situated on the delivery side and so weighted as to provide the minimum required pressure at the highest sprinkler head. The static pressure in the sprinkler system would keep the ram at the top of its travel until a sprinkler head was opened. When a

sprinkler head was opened the pressure in the system would fall and the weighted ram would then descend and, in doing so, would open the hydraulic mains valve thus admitting high-pressure water through the injector nozzle. While the system was in operation the ram would remain at the bottom of its travel, but when the system ceased to operate the pressure of the mixture of hydraulic power and low-pressure supply water built up thus raising the weighted ram to its topmost position, and shutting off the hydraulic power supply. To maintain the static pressure in the system it was, of course, necessary to have a non-return valve in the low-pressure supply pipe.

Cellar Pumps
Hydraulic jet pumps were eminently adaptable to the pumping out of cellars of waterside buildings subject to flooding and it was possible to make such installations automatic in action.

Machine Shop Practice
The earliest machine shops were usually powered by a steam engine which drove through a wide belt, or through ropes, a main shaft or shafts, which in turn, through fast and loose pulleys with the necessary striking gear, drove countershafts from which the machines were driven by three- or four-step cone pulleys. Today the integral electric drive is universal.

But before electricity supplies were available a number of pioneers visualized individual machine drives by means of hydraulic power, stressing the now obvious advantages of individual drives over line shafting. Today the predominating advantages of hydraulic operation where linear motion of the cutting tool is required, i.e., in shaping, planing, and slotting machines, are retained by the use of individual electrically driven pumps with oil as the operating fluid, while it is being pointed out that there are advantages in group hydraulic operation.

From the earliest days of the industrial revolution hydraulic power has maintained its supremacy for the operation of shaping, slotting, and planing machines. In Bramah's day a hydraulic planing machine was erected at Woolwich. In the middle of the last century a direct-acting hydraulic slotting machine was at work in the Elswick works of Armstrong Whitworths. This machine had a stroke of 4 ft, with a tumbling weight to reverse the motion, and was operated by water at a pressure of 700 lb/in². At the turn of the century it was being pointed out that a working pressure of 1500 lb/in² enabled the size of shop tools to be reduced and their portability and convenience in use increased.

Tweddell gave much attention to the development of hydraulic riveters and was responsible for a number of different forms both fixed and portable. It was claimed that the application of a combined blow and squeeze as applied by the hydraulic riveter prevented the formation of a shoulder on the rivet between the plates (such as was produced occasionally with machine riveting). Boilers riveted with hydraulic riveters were found to be steamtight without caulking.

Although there are no accounts of any extensive involvement by the public hydraulic power companies it is worth noting in passing that the advantages of the hydraulic operation of shop tools were early appreciated, that some of the advantages are still retained by using integral electric pumps for machine tool operation, and interest in this direction may well increase in view of the interim developments in hydraulic pumps and motors and the attention now being given to the potentialities of fluid power transmission.

CHAPTER FOUR

The Public Hydraulic Power Stations

4.1 HULL HYDRAULIC POWER COMPANY

Hull was the first town for which an Act of Parliament was obtained authorizing the laying of high-pressure hydraulic supply mains under the public thoroughfares to supply power to any potential customer. Hence Hull can claim to be the first town to have had a public power supply station.

The Act incorporating the company was passed in 1872 and stated the objects of the company to be to establish 'a system for applying motive power by hydraulic pressure to waterside and land cranes used for the purpose of raising and lowering goods and for working dock gates and other machinery'. The share capital was forty thousand pounds in four thousand shares of ten pounds each. The Act defined the boundaries of the district of the company. The western boundary was an imaginary line drawn along High Street, then along the property of the dock company, Dock Office Row, across Bridge Street, and along Trippett and Wincolmlee. The eastern boundary was Lime Street, Witham, Great Union Street, Harcourt Street, property of the dock company, and Tower Street. The northern boundary was the river at the point where the Barmston Drain falls therein, while the southern boundary was South Bridge Road, the river and Humber Street.

The Act empowered the company to draw water from the Old Harbour or the river Hull, at any point in its district, to an amount not exceeding one million gallons per day, provided it made half-yearly payments to the Kingston upon Hull Corporation at the rate of twelve pounds ten shillings (£12·50) for each two hundred and fifty thousand gallons, the water to be used for motive power purposes only. The company was also empowered under the Act to let or hire cranes, machines, engines or other appliances to be used in connection with its supply of power. The machinery was supplied by the Hydraulic Engineering Company of Chester and the pipes by the Staveley Coal and Iron Company.

The work was completed and the company became operational in 1876, the offices and pumping station being situated in Machell Street. The engine house there (Fig. 4.1) was designed to take four engine units of a nominal sixty horsepower, each unit consisting of

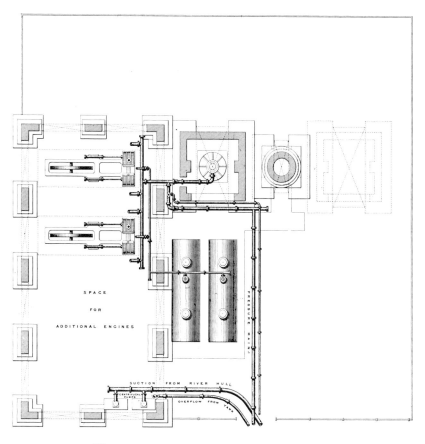

Fig. 4.1   HULL HYDRAULIC POWER STATION 1876

a pair of horizontal high-pressure pumping engines having cylinders of 12¼ in (311 mm) bore and 24 in (609·6 mm) stroke, taking steam at 100 lb/in² and capable of pumping 130 gallons per minute at 700 lb/in². The pumps were double acting, of the ram and piston type (Fig. 3.10(f)), the piston being 4⁹/₁₆ in (115·9 mm) and the ram 3⅛ in (79·4 mm) diameter. Initially only two units were installed, leaving two more to be erected when the demand warranted it. The demand must have justified their later installation for Ellington in 1895 (*Proc. Instn. Mech. Engrs.*) quoted 250 h.p. as the station output. The engine house was covered by a storage tank with filtering boxes through which the river water passed before being delivered to the pumping engines. The water was drawn from the river by an Appold centrifugal pump (in duplicate) through a 10 in pipe, the distance being 125 yd, after which the water was delivered into the tank, the total lift being 35 ft from low tide. Each pump was driven by a 4 in three-cylinder Brotherhood engine supplied with steam at 100 lb/in² and could deliver 800 gallons per minute. A 4 in return pipe from the tank to the river served as an overflow and as a means of cleaning the tank.

Steam was supplied by two Lancashire boilers each 22 ft 6 in long and 6 ft 6 in diameter. One accumulator was installed at Machelle Street with provision for an additional one, while another accumulator was sited at the corner of Grimsby Lane. The accumulator ram had a diameter of 18 in and a stroke of 20 ft, the tower in which it was housed being 45 ft high. The accumulator was loaded by a steel casing containing 57½ tons of copper slag and sand.

The line of the mains together with the chief features of the district boundaries are shown in Fig. 4.2. As originally laid the six-inch main had a total length of 1485 yd exclusive of the crossing of the Queen's Dock entrance, that on the north side of the dock entrance being 673 yd and that on the south side 812 yd. With the exception of the dock crossing the main was of cast iron with the usual spigot and faucet flanged joints with gutta percha jointing rings. Tee-pieces for 2 in, 3 in, and 4 in branches were placed at convenient points to permit of serice pipes being taken to consumers' premises. At the dock entrance the main was laid in a trench. The pipes were 6 in internal diameter made of welded iron

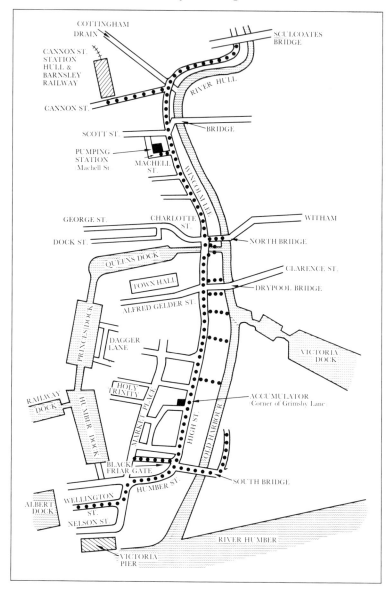

Fig. 4.2   MAP OF HULL HYDRAULIC POWER CO. MAINS

¾ in thick bent to a template made of the curves of the sides and bottom of the dock. The pipes were assembled at the dockside, tested to half a ton per square inch and then lowered into the trench, being then concreted to protect them from injury by ships' anchors, etc. Contemporary references to the work of the company are few and there is no record of its progressive development. R. H. Tweddell in the discussion on Ellington's paper of 1895 (*Proc. Instn. Mech. Engrs.*) observed that '. . . although the plan now appeared so simple, twenty years ago when the Hull scheme was started it did not meet with much encouragement, it seemed a leap in the dark of a most momentous kind. It proved, however, to be a great leap in the most satisfactory sense because the Hull works had paid steadily ever since. . . .' Ellington in his 1895 paper gave the weekly output of the Hull station as 100 000 to 500 000 gallons and the total length of the six-inch main as 2½ miles and the number of machines operated by it as 58. In addition there was the system of fire hydrants installed in High Street by the Corporation (p. 87) and there were sprinkler systems installed in factories, though there is no record of the number of these.

The manufacturers' drawings of the station plant were destroyed some time ago. The details quoted here have been taken mainly from the paper entitled 'The Transmission of Power to Distances' by Henry Robinson, *Proceedings of the Institution of Civil Engineers*, Vol. 49, 1877, and Fig. 4.1 is also from the same paper. Henry Robinson was the site engineer on the construction of the station, and Edward B. Ellington the consultant. The discussion on Robinson's paper was a long and interesting one and the serious student will find the report well worth reading in full as reflecting the diversity of contemporary opinion on the subject of power transmission.

That much valuable information has been irretrievably lost is but another indication of the need for a national repository and a recognized procedure for the preservation of old records.

Block layout plans of the area for the early years of the present century indicate a figure of 350 h.p. for the station output and a photograph of the interior of the engine house about the year 1907 (Fig. 4.3) shows three units of different sizes. No doubt by then there had been plant replacements, the new pumping engines

Fig. 4.3   HULL HYDRAULIC POWER COMPANY. INTERIOR OF ENGINE HOUSE. *c.* 1907

probably being compounds selected from those listed on p. 47. The general design appears similar to that of units shown in a catalogue of that period issued by the Hydraulic Engineering Company, which the author has been privileged to inspect. This, however, is purely a matter of conjecture unsupported by any available evidence.

The station suffered war damage in 1944 but continued to operate after the war. The company was wound up in 1947 when Mr F. J. Haswell who had been engineer and manager from 1904 retired.

All that remains today is the tank shown in Fig. 4.4 and the engine house below, which is now a works store. The mains along High Street are still there and their line can be traced by a number of inspection covers bearing the initials H.H.P.Co.

Although only a relatively small concern the Hull public hydraulic system was virtually the feasibility study for that of the London Hydraulic Power Company, the largest of the public hydraulic power companies and the last to survive.

4.2   LONDON HYDRAULIC POWER COMPANY

General Development

The London company started life as The Wharfs and Warehouses

Fig. 4.4   HULL HYDRAULIC POWER COMPANY. OUTSIDE OF BUILDING TODAY
Courtesy *Hull Daily Mail*

Steam Power and Hydraulic Pressure Company which was incorporated by Act of Parliament in 1871, but the powers granted
by the Act remained dormant until resuscitated in 1882, and
hydraulic power was not supplied under the Act until the autumn
of 1883 when there were some seven miles of mains on the north
and south banks of the River Thames, and the output of power
water was 340000 gallons per week. Under the original Act
operations were limited to a defined area. A new Act of Parliament
was passed in 1884 which changed the title of the company to The
London Hydraulic Power Company and extended the area of
operation. As a result there was a big increase in the number of
consumers. In December 1887 the length of the mains, which
were 7 in diameter, was 27 miles, the power water pumped per
week being 2062000 gallons and the horsepower provided 800. By
1895 the mains length was 76 miles, gallons per week 9500000,
and horsepower output 3400. At the turn of the century the
consumers included a number of railway depots. The steady increase in output continued until 1910 when the effect of competition from the electrical stations became apparent and from then

until 1926 the annual output was about static. In 1926 the acquisition of the supplies to the London and St Katharine's Docks, Surrey Commercial Docks, and the West India Docks increased the output by some 250 million gallons per annum. By 1927 the output had increased to 1651·5 million gallons with 8000 machines connected, and by the end of 1927 the length of the mains was 184 miles. But expansion terminated here and there was no further increase in the length of the mains. The annual output remained static until the outbreak of war in 1939, when the supplies to docks and railways represented thirty per cent of the total output.

With the heavy and continuous bombing of London the system obviously was very susceptible to war damage especially since within the boundary of the City of London the density of hydraulic machines was the greatest. For example, practically all the showrooms and offices of the textile industry, in nearly all of which some form of hydraulic lift was installed, were situated in an area approximately three-quarters of a mile square and this area was completely demolished. The firms concerned obtained accommodation outside the centre of London and when the sites were redeveloped electrical lifts were installed. A similar situation arose with site development all over London with the result that after the war the company concentrated its efforts on retaining the existing lifts already connected to the mains, and these numbered several hundred, and the installation of goods lifts and short-stroke direct-acting lifts for car showrooms and warehouses. A further influence has been the national policy of inducing industry to move out of London. The two factors, enemy action and the area post-war development policy were solely responsible for the reduction in output which by 1966 was 750 million gallons per annum.

The post-war period brought its problems of increased fuel and labour costs calling for the maximum economy in the use of fuel and the optimum degree of mechanization. Electrical development had proceeded apace and it appeared that the solution lay in electrification of the pump drives. How this was achieved is described in detail later. As a result the labour force engaged at the stations, which when under steam amounted to some 90 to 100 men, was, following electrification, reduced to 17. During the period of electrification, i.e., from 1953 to 1966, none of the redundant personnel was dismissed, the majority reaching retirement during the period while the remainder was accounted for by normal staff wastage. By 1973 only two stations were operational and the company went into voluntary liquidation in 1976.

The London Hydraulic Power Company was the largest of the public hydraulic power companies. The scope of its influence and the fields in which it met the demand for power at a time when other sources were not available or were uncompetitive are indications of the potentialities of public hydraulic power supply, even in its early days, as well as a measure of the success of the company.

The bascules of Tower Bridge, each weighing over 980 tons, were lifted by machinery operated from the company's mains as were hydraulic cranes in the docks of the Port of London Authority and on private wharfs, as well as cranes, wagon hoists, and lifts in railway depots.

In the entertainment world hydraulic power was used to operate fire curtains in such theatres as Her Majesty's, The Palace, Savile, Drury Lane, etc., the revolving stage at the Coliseum, the cabaret floor at the Savoy Hotel, and organ consoles at The Odeon, Marble Arch, and several other cinemas.

Several thousand hydraulic lifts were in operation in public and commercial buildings throughout the city for the transport of goods as well as passengers.

In the early days hydraulic power was even used for the generation on site of electricity for lighting and other purposes in successful competition with the early electric lighting companies, and compact units consisting of a Pelton wheel direct coupled to a dynamo were available, and hydraulic engines with belt driven generators were used for the same purpose.

Hydraulic power did not make a great impact on the domestic scene possibly due to the fact that in its day domestic labour was cheap and in plentiful supply. Had present-day conditions operated then possibly the story would have been different since the potentialities of hydraulic power were not less than those of electricity today. Small motors were available for the operation of appliances and in particular a vacuum cleaning service deserving of better notice was available.

Hotels were possibly better situated to make use of the facilities offered, and here hydraulic lifts were common. The hydraulic vacuum cleaner system was first introduced in the building of the Savoy and Simpsons Hotels in the Strand and the systems were in operation until 1937. The skirtings in the rooms and corridors were virtually vacuum chambers in which the vacuum was created by hydraulic ejectors. At intervals along the skirtings were a number of plug points to which the maid attached a flexible hose. The occasional inability of staff to replace the cap securely after use resulted in some loss of vacuum, but in general the system was silent and efficient.

The Pumping Stations

The first pumping station was erected on a site known as Falcon Wharf, on the south bank of the river some 200 yd east of Black-friars Bridge. By 1887 there were three stations in operation, Falcon Wharf, Philip Lane, and Kensington Court. Falcon Wharf was to beome a key station in the company's network but Philip Lane and Kensington Court, both starting as separate ventures, were ultimately destined to play an insignificant part in the development of the system.

Premises in the area bounded by Wood Street, Addle Street, Philip Lane, and London Wall had been destroyed by fire and hydraulic power was required for the new buildings. But the area was outside the operational district of the Wharfs and Warehouses Steam and Hydraulic Power Company, so a small pumping station was erected in Philip Lane to supply consumers in the neighbour-hood. Under the 1884 act the Philip Lane area was included in the operational area of the London Hydraulic Power Company and consequently the Philip Lane station became a stand-by, though the accumulator there was in constant connection with the mains, becoming a supplementary accumulator in the main system.

At Kensington Court a new estate was being built. Each house was to be fitted with a hydraulic lift so a special station was built for the express purpose of supplying power for these lifts. The station operating pressure was 450 lb/in², this being the pressure required by the lifts being installed. With the extension of the mains to Kensington it proved more economical to charge the Kensington Court accumulator loaded at 450 lb/in² from the 700 lb/in² mains (thus losing 250 lb/in²) than to work the smaller station, so that by 1893 Kensington Court had ceased to be a pumping station.

In 1887 a station was built at Millbank (Grosvenor Road) Westminster. This station contained similar plant to that at Falcon Wharf but it had a different water supply and worked at a higher steam pressure.

The output of the Millbank station was soon taken up and a further station was erected at Wapping on a site adjoining the Shadwell Tidal Basin of London Docks. This station had a greater capacity than either the Falcon Wharf or Millbank stations and the engines were triple expansion as against the compounds previously used, and worked at a higher steam pressure.

Another pumping station was built at City Road on a site on the Regents Canal with a capacity equal to that of Wapping, so that by 1895 there were four main stations in operation, i.e., Falcon Wharf, Millbank, Wapping, and City Road, with additional accumulators at Philip Lane and Kensington Court. Figure 4.5 shows a map of the system at that date.

The accumulators used in connection with the system were:

Two at Falcon Wharf 20 in ram diameter, 23 ft stroke;

One at Millbank 18 in ram diameter, 20 ft stroke;

One at Philip Lane 18 in ram diameter, 20 ft stroke;

Two at Wapping 20 in ram diameter, 23 ft stroke.

The one at Kensington Court has been omitted for it had a purely local function and had no influence on the main system.

The total capacity of the accumulators was 1600 gallons. The pumping capacity of the plant was 3500 gallons per minute. This shows that the main function of an accumulator is to regulate the pressure. It has little effect as regards storage of energy.

In 1903 a further station was erected at Rotherhithe similarly equipped to the Wapping station.

The varying fortunes of the company affected the stations and their development in different ways. The following is a short potted history of each of the main stations.

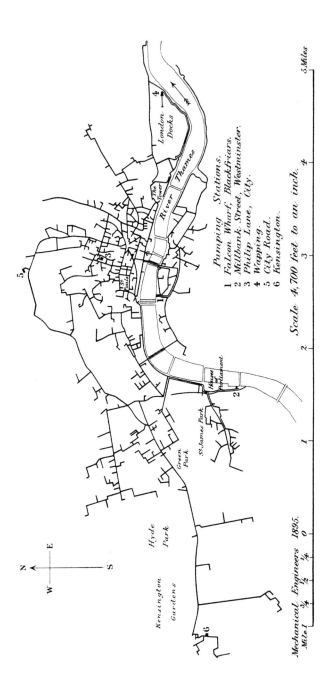

Fig. 4.5   LAYOUT OF LONDON HYDRAULIC POWER CO. MAINS AND PUMPING STATIONS

Falcon Wharf Station

A house on the site was a very old one said to have been occupied by Sir Christopher Wren during the building of Saint Paul's Cathedral. A few alterations were made to this to enable it to be used as offices for the company and a dwelling for one of the staff. The rest of the site was cleared to accommodate the station. The engine house contained four sets of pumping engines of the type already mentioned on p. 48 and shown in Fig. 3.5. These vertical compounds were capable of developing 200 indicated horsepower and combined the advantages of the three-throw pump with that of direct connection between pump plungers and engine pistons. The centre cylinder was the HP with a bore of 19 in. The two outer LP cylinders had a bore of 25 in, the stroke being 24 in. The pumps were single acting with a plunger diameter of 5 in. Surface condensers were fitted to each engine and the auxiliaries (air, circulating, and feed pumps) were worked from a beam linked with the HP cylinder cross-head in accordance with marine practice. Each unit was capable of delivering 240 gallons of water per minute at 750 lb/in^2 with a piston speed of 200 ft/min, but it could be worked at a piston speed of 250 ft/min giving a maximum delivery of 300 gallons per minute. During a trial in 1887 one of the engines was run continuously at a constant speed of 55.35 rev/min when the consumption of rough small coal was 2.19 lb per indicated horsepower hour. In everyday performance the rate was 2.93 lb per i.h.p. hour, the increase of one-third being due to the varying speed of the engines.

The boilers were of the Lancashire type with Galloway tubes, four in number, three being 7 ft in diameter by 28 ft long, and one 7 ft 6 in diameter by 28 ft long, all being fitted with Vicars' mechanical stokers. A Green's economizer with 96 tubes was fitted at the back of the boilers. The economizer and stoker gear were driven by a Brotherhood three-cylinder hydraulic engine having cylinders 3 in bore and 3 in stroke. The working steam pressure was 80 lb/in^2.

The two accumulators having rams 20 in diameter with a stroke of 23 ft, had weight cases filled with slag to give a working pressure of 750 lb/in^2 and each was fitted with an electric bell coming into operation when the accumulator was half down thus signalling to the engineer in charge to be ready to start another engine.

The water storage tanks formed the roofs of the engine and boiler houses, and the water for the power supply was pumped from the River Thames into the tank on the engine house which was 50 ft by 45 ft by 8 ft deep, with a capacity of 105 500 gallons, divided into three compartments providing virtually three separate tanks. The river water was very muddy and the mud had to be got rid of by settlement and filtration before the water passed to the pressure pumps.

The filtered water tank was 66 ft by 30 ft by 8 ft deep with a capacity of 92 800 gallons. This tank was divided into two compartments, a portion of one of the compartments being partitioned off to form two charcoal filter beds, each filter bed measuring 15 ft by 12½ ft.

The filtered water tank, which was over the boiler house, was 7 ft below the level of the unfiltered water tank so filtration proceeded by gravity. The charcoal beds were intended only to remove the fine particles passing the mechanical filters. These mechanical filters consisted of cast-iron cylinders 5 ft in diameter arranged in groups of two, one above the other. Each cylinder contained a movable perforated piston and a perforated diaphragm. Between the piston and diaphragm was a quantity of broken sponge which was compressed by a hydraulic ram. After between four and six hours operation the flow became seriously impeded by the clogging of the filter. The filter was cleaned by reversing the flow of water, opening the connection to the washout pipes and causing the perforated piston to move up and down in the cylinder thus alternately compressing and releasing the sponge. By thus rinsing the mass of sponge the filter became clean in about fifteen minutes and filtering could then continue. The capacity of each group of two was 5000 gallons per hour and five groups were used giving a total filtering capacity of 25 000 gallons per hour. Filtering was a continuous process proceeding day and night. As an emergency reserve a supply of water was available from the local water company.

The water was pumped from the river to the tanks by steam-driven pumps. Arrangements were also made so that the engine condenser circulating pumps could be used for pumping water from the river but this method was not very satisfactory on account of the long length of suction pipe and the constantly changing engine speeds.

One suction pipe drew water from a sump in the foreshore while the other drew from a cast-iron box placed 185 ft from the quay and provided with means of clearing the box of any deposit which could collect in it. A considerable quantity of mud settled in the unfiltered water tanks over the engine house so the water was conveyed to the filters through swivel pipes provided with floats so that the water passing to the filters was taken from the surface. Each compartment had a swivel pipe. When river water was being pumped into a compartment its swivel pipe would be put out of use. The circulating water for the engine condensers was taken from one of the tanks over the engine house and was returned to one of the other tanks. During filtration the temperature of the water was lowered and the water was further cooled during its stay in the filtered water tanks. Arrangements were available whereby should the temperature of the water in the unfiltered water tanks rise above 90°F water was pumped from the river and returned to the river. During winter filtered water could be used as condenser cooling water so as to raise its temperature. By these means the water delivered into the hydraulic supply mains was maintained all the year round at a temperature between 60° and 85°F. In this way the possibility of frost damage to the mains was minimized and a satisfactory solution of the cooling water problem provided.

Operational experience showed that the method of getting water from the river was not entirely satisfactory. With the lowest spring tides there was an appreciable interval when it was not possible to draw water from the river and there were occasions when the capacity of the storage tanks was insufficient to tide over this interval. Meanwhile the Millbank station had been built and following the successful exploitation of wells at this station it was decided to reclaim part of the foreshore at Falcon Wharf and sink wells with headings under the river into the gravel bed. But not more than 10000 gallons of water per hour were obtained in this way. Consequently it was necessary to continue getting the major portion of the water used from the river though the wells ensured an adequate quantity of water being available at all states of the tide. Also reclamation of the foreshore provided much needed room for pipe storage.

Experience at Millbank also demonstrated the superiority of hydraulic pumps so that the steam-driven pumps originally used for pumping water from the river were superseded by hydraulic pumps with an appreciable decrease in the steam consumption of the station.

The offices of the company were later moved to Millbank.

Millbank Station

The construction of this station was started in 1887 and its design was based on experience gained at Falcon Wharf. The engines and boilers were of the same type but the steam pressure was increased to 100 lb/in² and the water was drawn from a well instead of the river, as the methods first adopted for getting water from the river at Falcon Wharf were not altogether satisfactory. The average yield of the well was 300000 gallons per 24 hours which was adequate for the station capacity, and the total capacity of the filtered and unfiltered water tanks over the engine house was made equal to this. The water was pumped from the well to the tanks by hydraulic pumps (Fig. 4.6) instead of the steam pumps originally used at Falcon Wharf. Hydraulic power was not supplied from this station during the night but pumping from the well and filtering of the water went on continuously, the hydraulic pumps being independent of the working of any particular station so long as the mains pressure in the general system was maintained. The filtered water tanks were placed over the boiler house at a lower level, the difference in level between them and the engine house tanks being used to overcome the resistance of the filters to the passage of the water. Treatment of the water was necessary for although the water was bright and clear when coming from the well, on exposure to the air it turned a reddish yellow and precipitated iron oxide. Consequently the water was given a preliminary aeration by allowing the water from the rising main to fall over fountains. Most of the iron oxide was precipitated in the upper tanks. The water was then treated with lime, not so much to soften it, though the hardness was reduced, as to bring down the remaining iron oxide. The water then flowed through the filter presses.

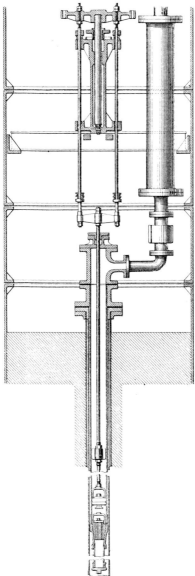

Fig. 4.6   DEEP WELL PUMP

(Proc. Instn Civ. Engrs 1887)

The compound engines were replaced in 1910 by triple-expansion engines of the type which had proved successful in stations built later, i.e., Wapping, City Road, and Rotherhithe.

In the first stage of the post-war electrification programme mentioned on p. 98, these triple-expansion engines were modified by replacing the flywheel by a double helical gear through which the pumps were driven giving a 10 to 1 reduction in speed from a 270 h.p. 3300 volt a.c. constant speed motor. The cylinder castings were left in place so as to retain the box structure and to use the piston rods as additional guides. This conversion, completed in 1953, proved very satisfactory, the pumps operating at a constant speed of 49·8 rev/min with an output of 360 gallons per minute at 850 lb/in².

When later in the programme a system of remote control from Wapping was installed it was not found practicable to remotely control these pumping engines and in view of this two were removed and replaced by electrically driven three-throw pumps. The interior of the station then is shown in Fig. 4.7.

Wapping Station
With the increasing demand for power it became apparent that a third station was necessary. By then appreciable experience had been obtained and opinions had crystallized. In 1892 a station was built at Wapping on a site adjoining the Shadwell Tidal Basin of London Docks, to accommodate six sets of engines each of 200 indicated horsepower of the same general construction as the vertical compounds at Millbank and Falcon Wharf but made triple expansion with cylinders of 15 in, 22 in, and 36 in bore and a stroke of 24 in working at a steam pressure of 150 lb/in². The boilers were of the Fairbairn–Beeley type, Vicars' mechanical stokers being fitted to all boilers. It was felt at the time that this represented the optimum size of station and the pumping engines the ideal standard units for the purpose. Wapping then was the first of three similar stations. The type of pumping engine became very popular and a large number were supplied by the Hydraulic Engineering Company of Chester to the London Hydraulic Power Company and other hydraulic power concerns.

Hydraulic pumps delivered water from a well into two compart-

Fig. 4.7 LONDON HYDRAULIC POWER
Interior of Millbank (Grosvenor Road) Pumping Station

ments of the tank over the boiler house. Any additional water required was obtained from the dock. The capacity of the un-filtered water tanks was 150000 gallons. There was a filter house on the level of the stoke-hole floor containing eight filters. After the water had passed through the filters it was collected in an under-ground clear water reservoir having two sections. The engine circulating water pumps drew water from this reservoir and after it had passed through the engine condenser the water was returned to the remaining two compartments of the tank over the boiler house from which the main pumps drew their supply, it being necessary to have a head on the suction side of the power pumps. The total capacity of the tanks and reservoirs was 800000 gallons, this being approximately the 24 hour delivery of power water from the station.

The water filtering medium was a bed of animal charcoal which was cleaned by reverse flow whilst a jet of steam was used to send a current of air into the filters with the water. This resulted in violent ebullition and complete cleaning of the charcoal.

As in the case of Millbank, pumping from the well and filtration of the water proceeded continuously day and night, but normally the engines only ran twelve hours in twenty-four, the variations in power demand being met by the Falcon Wharf central station, this being effected by delivering the water into the mains at the out stations at a higher pressure than the central station.

Later (date unknown) two electrically driven turbine pumps were installed for service only during times of peak load, thus bringing the capacity of the station up to 3500 gallons per minute at a pressure of 850 lb/in^2.

In 1926 the station underwent a major reconstruction when additional pumping equipment was installed. This consisted of a nine-stage turbine pump made by Mather and Platt, driven through gearing by a Parsons steam turbine, this new plant being capable of supplying 1000 gallons per minute against a pressure of 850 lb/in^2 and capable of taking a large part of the constant load of the station. Steam was supplied to the various pumps by three Babcock and Wilcox boilers having an evaporative capacity of 25 500 lb/h, steam being generated at 150 lb/in^2. These boilers were fitted with chain grate stokers. The coal was brought to the station by barges and was raised by grabs and automatically conveyed to the boiler house hoppers.

The station was reconstructed to serve as both a power station and a demonstration showroom having an effective display of miscellaneous plant operated by hydraulic power. Amongst the display items of that time were the automatic injector – the 'equivalent of a fire engine', a 24-in Pelton wheel driving a Mather and Platt centrifugal pump delivering 1000 gallons per minute against a head of 50 ft, a hydraulically operated deep well pump, and a vertical injector using high-pressure water to create a vacuum for cleaning purposes. With a permanent pipe system the cleaner hoses could be connected wherever they were required and all the dirt passed away with the water into the drains.

By the end of the war the public hydraulic supply industry faced with the rapid growth and phenomenal success of the electrical supply industry had its back to the wall fighting for survival. All thoughts of expansion had gone, consolidation being the order of the day. The time was fast approaching when survival would depend on exploiting the unassailable suitability for hoist, press, lift, and crane operation of hydraulic power and facing the economic fact that the best way of doing that was by the conversion of electrical energy. Ultimately the industry was to become reconciled to the philosophy 'if you can't beat them join them', but the immediate prevailing mood was one of obstinate defiance, and refusal to make any concession to the 'enemy'. Even as late as 1946 operatives at Wapping went about their duties using the old stokehold type of paraffin lamp while the chain grate stokers were still driven by a Pelton wheel. For this information I am indebted to Mr Donnachie who was station superintendent at Wapping from 1946.

When the post-war electrification programme was implemented, owing to the age of the steam engines conversion along the lines of that at Millbank was considered undesirable so two sets of electrically driven three-throw reciprocating pumps were installed each with a capacity of 200 gallons per minute, fitted with Ward Leonard variable speed gear governed from a small accumulator 3 in diameter by 10 ft stroke. These units proved so efficient that the use of the large accumulators previously essential to take up the momentary fluctuations in output, could be dispensed with.

The three-throw pump units have a much higher pumping efficiency than the centrifugal type. The electrification procedure set a pattern for the conversions at the City Road and Rotherhithe stations.

During the modifications at Wapping Messrs Metropolitan Vickers (now AEI) devised a method of remote control of all the pumping units at the various stations of the Company by means of the Post Office telephone lines with Wapping as the master station, making it possible for Wapping to control Rotherhithe, City Road, Millbank, and East Dock stations.

City Road Station

In 1893 a fourth station was built on a site on the Regents Canal in Wharf Road, City Road, modelled on Wapping and with the same capacity as the Wapping Station at that time. The water supply was taken from the canal, the filtration being similar to that at Wapping.

Rotherhithe Station

This station was built in 1903 to accommodate eight triple-expansion engines of the standard type, and generally modelled on Wapping. It was the fifth and last steam station of a network with stations located at strategic points of the city.

The East Dock Station formed part of the docks supplies acquired much later (see p. 98).

4.3 LIVERPOOL HYDRAULIC POWER

The Liverpool Hydraulic Power Co was inaugurated in 1888 under Acts of Parliament of 1884 and 1887, thus being the third oldest concern. It then had 18 miles of 6-in main, an initial installed horsepower of 800 and a working pressure of 700 lb/in². The water supply was taken from the Leeds and Liverpool canal and filtered.

By 1890 there were thirty miles of mains extending through the business area of the city from Bootle to Toxteth. Additional plant had been installed so that by this time there were two pumping stations. One station and the offices of the Resident Engineer and Manager were situated at the north end of the town in Athol Street and the other at the south end in Grafton Street. The total pumping plant consisted of nine vertical triple expansion units capable of delivering 18000 gallons of water per hour, the power being supplied continuously day and night. The power was used for lifts (passenger and goods), cranes, packing and pressing various materials, and also through hydrants and sprinklers for fire-fighting purposes. By 1895 some 453 machines were in operation off the system and the total water delivered was one million gallons per week.

Its Acts of 1884 and 1887 gave the company compulsory powers to lay mains in certain prescribed areas and permissive powers to lay mains in further districts with the sanction of Liverpool Corporation. The *Liverpool Review* for 9 February 1889 contained complaints that the Health Committee of the Corporation 'had seriously and needlessly hampered the operations of the company by preventing it from laying its mains in certain streets where they are desired'. It appeared that the Corporation was prepared to supply water from the domestic supply mains for the operation of

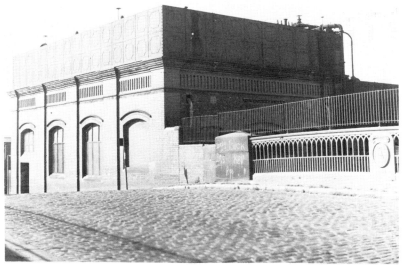

Fig. 4.8 LIVERPOOL HYDRAULIC POWER
Athol Street Pumping Station. Courtesy Merseyside County Museums

lifts and attempted to exclude the Hydraulic Power Co from entering into competition with it by preventing the company wherever possible from laying its own mains under the streets.

The dispute is of interest as incidentally providing a comparison of contemporary costs and the advantages of a high-pressure supply as compared with a low-pressure one.

It appears that although hydraulic mains had already been laid in Tithebarn Street and Bixteth Street and Lower Castle Street, permission had been frequently refused for extensions from the mains in any of these streets to supply the Exchange Co, the Liverpool and London and Globe Insurance Co, the British and Foreign Marine Insurance Co, and the Prudential Assurance Co, a total of some eight lifts which in the absence of a high-pressure supply would be operated from the Corporation mains. The eight lifts would consume approximately six million gallons of Corporation water per quarter at 7d (3p) per 1000 gallons giving a total cost of £175 per quarter. With the high-pressure supply to do the same work would necessitate the use of only 400000 gallons, owing to the difference in pressure, and the total cost would amount to £85, representing a saving of £90 per quarter.

Greater cost is not, however, the only drawback of low-pressure operation. Low-pressure lifts are much slower than high-pressure ones and less efficient. A specific case was quoted of a lift in African Chambers, Old Hall Street, which, previously operating from the Corporation mains, had been converted to high-pressure operation. This lift used 78000 gallons of high-pressure water at a cost of £16 14s 5d (£16·72). Previously it consumed 1370065 gallons of Corporation water at a total cost of £39 19s 2d (£39·96) per quarter. With the Corporation supply and three persons in the cage the time for the 56 ft travel was 38 seconds while with the high pressure supply the time was 15 seconds and higher speeds could be obtained if desired. Lift speed is of particular significance with warehouse lifts where the rapid handling of goods is of importance.

The Athol Street station was electrified about 1960. Operations ceased in 1971 and on closure of the station the pumping plant at Athol Street consisted of:

Three, three-throw electrically driven pumps by Ward Lennox each with a delivery of 100 gallons per minute, and

*Three, three-throw electrically driven pumps by Hathorn Davey, each with a delivery of 150 gallons per minute.

The three large pumps were bought secondhand, having worked at King's Cross railway station since 1924.

Figure 4.8 shows the outside of the Athol Street building and Fig. 4.9 the interior just prior to closure, while Fig. 4.10 is a close-up view of one of the large three-throw pumps (ex King's Cross).

4.4   GLASGOW HYDRAULIC POWER

In Glasgow there was already a substantial demand for hydraulic power before the high-pressure system was installed, as some 600

Fig. 4.9   LIVERPOOL HYDRAULIC POWER
Interior of Athol Street Station just prior to closure showing the three smaller (Ward Lennox) pumping units. Courtesy Merseyside Museums.

* One of these pumps, items of equipment, company documents, and photographic coverage of Athol St Station before dismantling, are available at the Merseyside County Museums, William Brown St, Liverpool.

Fig. 4.10   LIVERPOOL HYDRAULIC POWER
One of the larger (Hathorn Davey) pumping units ex King's Cross. Courtesy
Merseyside Museums.

or so hydraulic hoists were being worked from the Corporation
waterworks supply and about a hundred hydraulic presses were
known to exist within the city boundary. There was as a con-
sequence considerable variation in the pressure of the domestic
supply. A private company intimated its intention of meeting the
demand for hydraulic power but it withdrew when the Water
Commissioners indicated their intention of introducing a high-
pressure supply for power purposes in order to get rid of the
embarrassing variation of pressure in the water supply mains.

The contracts for the work apart from the cost of the station site
totalled £54000, a large sum in those days, so the successful
development of the scheme would have called for a strong commercial company, apart from which it had been made clear that
the Corporation would not readily grant permission for the
opening up of the ten miles or so of thoroughfare through which it
was proposed to carry pipes.

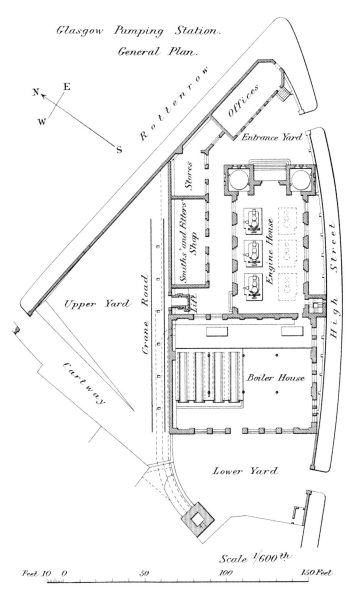

Fig. 4.11   GLASGOW HYDRAULIC POWER SUPPLY. PLAN OF STATION

The appeal to the consumer centred around the saving to be effected, it being instanced that a consumer paying £70 for water to operate a hoist from the low-pressure supply would, with a high-pressure supply be called upon to pay only £40. The advantage to the Corporation was the considerable saving in the quantity of domestic water used.

An Act of Parliament was obtained in 1892. A year elapsed before work was started. The system became operational on 30 May 1895. The system was designed by Messrs Ellington and Woodall of Westminster and it followed the Manchester pattern.

The site chosen for the pumping station was at the corner of High Street and Rotten Row, a triangular piece of ground then occupied by some derelict old houses which were demolished. Figure 4.11 is the site plan. The ground sloped downwards towards

Fig. 4.12   GLASGOW HYDRAULIC POWER PUMPING STATION, 295 HIGH STREET
Built in red sandstone with three crenellated towers, the roof water storage being hidden by a crenellated wall. Courtesy Strathclyde Regional Archives.

High Street and advantage was taken of this to construct a series of castellated buildings to harmonize with the surroundings (Fig. 4.12).

Following the lead of Manchester and bearing in mind the demand for power for pressing, the supply pressure was fixed at half a ton per square inch. The station was designed to take six vertical triple expansion pumping engines but initially only three were installed (Fig. 4.11). Provision was made for eight Lancashire boilers 7 ft diameter, 30 ft long, as it was proposed to use coke breeze as fuel. Initially only four boilers were installed. Green's economizers were fitted similar to those at Manchester and similarly the two accumulators had rams 18 in diameter with a stroke of 23 ft. Figure 4.13 shows a section through the station at this time and Fig. 4.14 the mains layout. The largest mains were made 7 in diameter (as against 6 in at Manchester) as the Glasgow water had a corrosive effect which gave rise to a tendency to reduction of the bore. Each pumping engine delivered into one of the four 7-in mains so arranged that they formed two separate circuits one circuit to the north of Argyll Street and the other to the south. Cross connecting valves were located at certain points to permit the system being worked as one or two separate circuits. In the streets were 6-in and 5-in pipes connected with the main delivery pipes, each fitted with a valve so that any street could be cut off from the main circuit when necessary.

The chimney stack of the station was octagonal in section, 160 ft high with a battlemented crown giving it a distinctive character in tone with the surroundings. The engine house was 76 ft long by 40 ft wide and the boiler house 84 ft long by 64 ft wide. The water storage tank over the boiler house contained 200 000 gallons of water. The water supply was obtained from the Corporation domestic mains so no filtering was involved.

By 1900 there were about 17 miles of hydraulic supply pipes laid in the streets of the city. The water supplied during the year 1900–1901 was 125 788 gallons per day, the total cost of the works had been upwards of £113 000 and the revenue derived was £8255 per annum.

A Water Department report of 1933 stated that the hydraulic station was then equipped with five sets of triple expansion

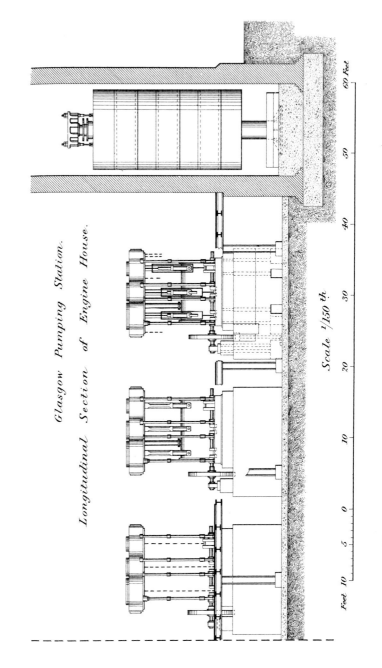

Glasgow Pumping Station.

Longitudinal Section of Engine House.

Scale 1/150th.

Feet 10 5 0 10 20 30 40 50 60 Feet

Fig. 4.13 GLASGOW HYDRAULIC POWER STATION. SECTION THROUGH ENGINE HOUSE

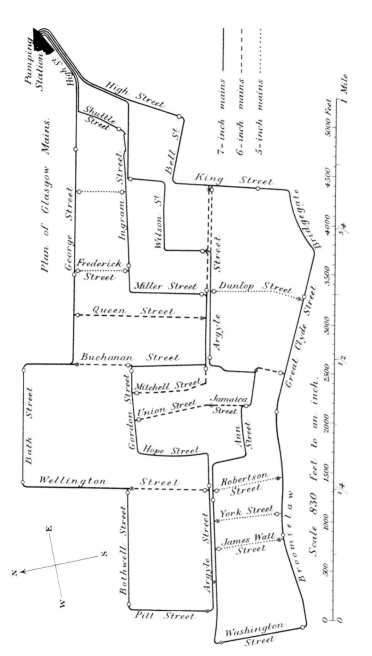

Fig. 4.14 GLASGOW HYDRAULIC POWER SUPPLY – MAINS LAYOUT

pumping engines delivering pressure water at all times at a pressure of 900 lb/in² and that rapid development of the motor industry round about that time had resulted in a demand for the application of hydraulic power to garage car washing plants in addition to the more general uses for hoists, cranes, packing presses, riveting machines, etc.

The supply of hydraulic power was discontinued on 31 August 1964. The triple expansion pumping engines had been removed and the station electrified, but no date or particulars are available other than that on closure of the station surplus electrical equipment was sold to Manchester (p. 126).

4.5   MANCHESTER HYDRAULIC POWER

In Manchester the Corporation took the initiative and in 1891 obtained an Act of Parliament 'to supply water under pressure for such purposes as water power is applicable'. The system became operational in 1894. A municipal concern has the advantage that it does not have to seek powers, or special permission, to lay mains under public thoroughfares, nor is it involved in any associated problems arising from the subsequent need for mains maintenance.

The choice of the supply pressure was influenced by the fact that it was anticipated that one of the main applications of hydraulic power would be for cotton baling. Equipment in existing establishments had been designed for an initial squeeze pressure of half a ton per square inch with arrangements for the final squeeze to be supplied by supplementary pumps or intensifiers. A further consideration was that as a general rule the higher the pressure the greater the economy of working. Consequently it was decided to supply water at a pressure of 1120 lb/in².

The equipment of the pumping station was broadly based on accepted conclusions from operational experience in London. The station was sited in Whitworth Street West, Oxford Street, and was designed to accommodate six sets of vertical triple expansion pumping engines, each of 200 h.p. supplied with steam by five Lancashire boilers each 7 ft 6 in diameter by 30 ft long. The steam pressure was 120 lb/in² this being the choice of the Corporation Committee concerned. Later the committee decided to add to the

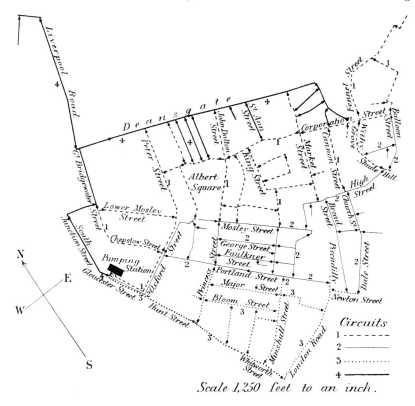

Scale 1,250 feet to an inch.

Fig. 4.15   MANCHESTER MAINS LAYOUT

boilers Watnum automatic circulating apparatus for increasing their efficiency. Two Green's economizers with 160 tubes each were fitted at the back of the boilers.

The Whitworth Street West Station became operational on 30 January 1894. By 1895 there were twelve miles of six-inch diameter mains, the station output was one million gallons per week, and there were 247 machines working off the system. Figure 4.15 shows a plan of the mains layout at that date and Fig. 4.16 the station layout (Whitworth Street).

Soon the Whitworth Street Station was working to capacity so another station was built adjacent to an arm of the Rochdale canal in Pott Street, Ancoats. This station initially contained four sets of pumping engines but finally there were seven triple expansion pumping engines, six of 210 i.h.p. pumping 240 gallons per minute at 60 rev/min and one of 350 i.h.p. pumping 325 gallons per minute at 60 rev/min, steamed by five Lancashire boilers, 7 ft 6 in by 30 ft working at 130 lb/in². The Pott Street station became operational on 6 July 1899.

With increasing demand a third station was built at Water Street and this commenced pumping on 14 October 1909. The four Lancashire boilers were 8 ft diameter by 30 ft long and supplied steam at 135 lb/in². The coal was delivered by boats on the River Irwell. There were six triple expansion engines each of 210 i.h.p. delivering 240 gallons of water at 60 rev/min.

The ancillary equipment at the three stations was very similar. Each had two hydraulic accumulators having 18 in diameter rams with a travel of 23 ft and casings weighing approximately 125 tons. In all three cases water was obtained from boreholes and delivered into overhead tanks originally by an air-lift system which was replaced in 1948 by submersible pumping sets. The borehole at Whitworth Street was typical, being 613 ft deep reducing in diameter from 19 in at the top to 9 in at the bottom. The compressed air was taken down the borehole by a 2-in pipe placed inside a 7 in water delivery pipe, and the air was injected into the water at a depth of 394 ft. The air–water mixture rose in the annular space between the air pipe and the 7 in water delivery pipe owing to the difference in weight of the water surrounding the 7 in delivery pipe and the water–air mixture inside.

Each station had its own workshop, air compressor house, and electric lighting plant. The meter testing house was at Whitworth Street.

All consumers were metered at the inlet side, i.e., at 1000 lb/in² by means of Kent High Pressure Uniform Meters.

The total consumption of power water reached a peak of 360 million gallons a year in the 1920s with a maximum number of consumers of 600. Electrification, started in 1922, was mainly confined to the Whitworth Street station where four of the original steam engines were removed and two base load multi-stage centrifugal pumps installed, between 1922 and 1924. In 1925 the

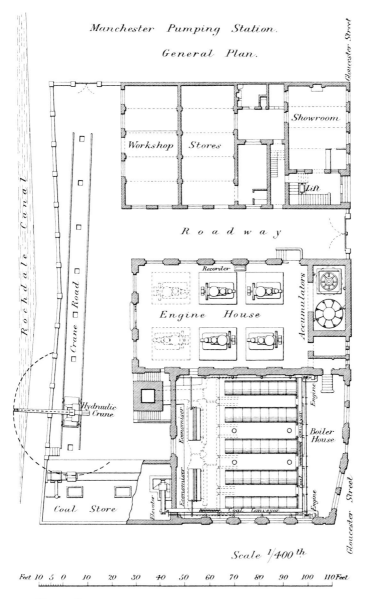

Fig. 4.16 MANCHESTER HYDRAULIC POWER. PLAN OF STATION

remaining two steam pumping engines were electrified by the removal of the steam cylinders and the flywheels. In place of the flywheels double helical reduction gear drives were fitted, thus converting each engine to a three-throw pump with plungers 4⁹/16 in diameter and 2 ft stroke, driven by a 220 h.p., 220 volt d.c. motor with a speed range of 375/750 rev/min and this involved a 500 kW motor converter to convert the high tension a.c. supply to low tension d.c. for the two variable speed motors. The two centrifugal pumps delivered 750 and 1100 gallons of power water per minute at 1120 lb/in² respectively when running at 1475 rev/min and were driven by motors of 1000 and 1250 b.h.p. The larger pump at that time was the largest pump of its type running in the United Kingdom. The original accumulators were retained. Water Street station was electrified afterwards (Fig. 4.17).

By 1930 contraction of the demand was apparent. This trend continued so that in 1939 Pott Street Station was closed. By the early 1960s difficulties made it necessary to give consideration to the future of the service. The six engines at Water Street, although well maintained and in reasonable mechanical condition were ageing. The 500 kW rotary converter at Whitworth Street was second-hand when installed and it was understood that the converter was made in 1914. The age of all the electrical equipment at Whitworth Street was the cause of some anxiety. The maximum length of the street mains was reached in 1948 and was then approximately 35½ miles. Since that time a policy of abandonment had been pursued so that by 1968 the active length was 26 miles. Corrosion and the risks of bursts in an ageing system carrying 1000 lb/in² gave rise to further concern.

By 1964 the Glasgow Corporation Hydraulic Power Supply had been abandoned and the Manchester Committee sought to purchase the surplus equipment. So in 1964 the two high-speed horizontal reciprocating pump units with 240 b.h.p. motors and an output of 250 gallons per minute were installed at Whitworth Street and one of the old converted steam engines was scrapped together with the two centrifugal pumps. These reciprocating pumps were kept available at Whitworth Street as a stand-by in case of trouble at Water Street Station. They were high-output fixed-speed sets suitable only for base load purposes and were not

Fig. 4.17 MANCHESTER HYDRAULIC POWER
Interior of Water Street Pumping Station just prior to closure in 1972, showing three of the six pumping units and how electrification had been carried out by the removal of the steam cylinders and replacement of the flywheels by geared electrical drives. The building remains, being subject to a preservation order. Courtesy Dr R. L. Hills.

suitable for periods of small demand, but nevertheless they gave cover against emergencies until the supply was terminated.

In 1968 the Waterworks Committee gave four years notice of closure to consumers. Then the number of consumers was approximately 120 and the annual consumption of water two million gallons.

A formal ceremony was held on 28 December 1972 at the Water Street pumping station when the Chairman of the Waterworks Committee stopped the pumps. The converted pumping engines were removed but the Water Street building remains. The pumps and equipment at Whitworth Street were disposed of as scrap and the building demolished.

4.6 · BIRMINGHAM HYDRAULIC SUPPLY SYSTEM

This system became operational under the Corporation Water Department in 1891, the pumping station being situated in Dalton Street. It was different from the other supply systems in several respects. Firstly the somewhat specialized power needs of the area were being largely met by a compressed air system, secondly the total installed power was less than that of any other public station, and thirdly the pumps were driven by gas engines.

Its existence had been anticipated for several years prior to its inception, and for some time previously water mains suitable for a pressure of 700 to 800 lb/in² had been laid, particularly in streets where the magnitude of the traffic had resulted in the replacement of macadamized roads by wood paving, such anticipation of future requirements being considered more desirable than later incurring the cost and inconvenience of taking up wood paving.

Gas engines were chosen since they were unlikely to cost more than steam engines and they offered the advantages of compactness, cleanliness, requiring the minimum amount of attention, and the absence of coal, ashes, feed water, smoke, and boiler repairs. A chimney stack was, however, necessary for the disposal of exhaust gases.

Three sets of engines and pumps were installed, one being of twelve nominal horsepower the other two being each of twenty nominal horsepower, the engines being of the Otto 'Silent' type manufactured by Messrs Crossley Brothers Limited. The main engine dimensions were

	12 horsepower	*20 horsepower*
Cylinder Bore, inches	11½	14
Stroke, inches	18	20
Speed, rev/min	160	160.

All the engines were fitted with two flywheels and were fixed on brick and cement foundations, the spaces between the foundations being occupied by air, gas, exhaust, and cylinder cooling water pipes. The engines were supplied with gas by service pipes, 3 in diameter in the case of the 12 h.p. engine and 4 in in the case of the 20 h.p. engines, these pipes being fed from an outside 9 in main. The supply to each engine was separately metered.

The engines drove countershafts by means of leather belts and the countershafts drove horizontal three-throw pumps through gearing. The drive and pump details were

	12 h.p. set	*20 h.p. sets*
Diameter of pump plungers, inches	2·5	3
Stroke, inches	10	12
Displacement of each plunger, cubic inches	49·08	84·82
Ratio of gearing	1 to 2·526	1 to 3·058
Diameter of driving pulley, inches	36·50	54
Diameter of driven pulley, inches	50·25	60
Hydraulic pressure, lb/in²	820	820

Space was reserved for the extension of the station building so as to provide for the installation of a further three pumping units later. The water was obtained from the town supply. A six-inch service main was brought into the station and from this main three-inch branch pipes were taken to the engine cylinder jackets and then to a six-inch suction main to which were connected the branch suction pipes of the hydraulic pumps so that the water on its way to the pressure pumps was used to cool the gas engine cylinders. From the pumps the high-pressure water passed to two six-inch delivery mains and to the accumulators. The delivery mains were of cast iron 1¼ in thick with the usual flanged joints and gutta-percha rings. The two mains formed a ring to supply a network of street mains. There were two accumulators housed in two towers in front of the station. Each had a ram 18 in in diameter with a stroke of 20 ft, the load being about 93 tons. Controls were installed to prevent the ram being pumped too high. These acted upon by-pass or relief valves which successively short-circuited the pump outputs to suction. When the pumps were thus rendered inoperative a wire connected to the actuating rope of the by-pass valve was made to lift the governor weight of the engine so that while idling the plant ran at a greatly reduced speed with a corresponding reduced consumption of gas.

The combined effect of the exhausts from the three engines could have been a nuisance to the neighbourhood since it was reported that 'the discharge from a plain exhaust pipe (from one engine) resembles the report of a gun'. Between the foundations of the engines and the pumps a double brick flue was built some 4 ft 6 in high by 2 ft wide, one end of which connected to the base of a fresh air inlet while the other end was connected to the base of the chimney stack which was 3 ft diameter inside by 50 ft high. The exhaust pipes from the engines were led into the horizontal flue where they terminated in bends facing towards the chimney stack. Each bend had a perforated plug consisting of a group of wrought-iron tubes half an inch in diameter of lengths varying from 3 to 4 ft. The ejection of the exhaust gases towards the chimney induced a flow of air from the fresh air inlet. At first it was thought that if the fresh air entry was at yard level the noise would be sufficiently subdued but it was found necessary to build a vertical shaft 15 ft high fitted with transverse baffle walls, and then it was practically impossible to detect any sound at all and the exhaust gases mixed with a large volume of fresh air were discharged silently at a height of 50 ft above ground level.

A gas engine has to be given a few initial revolutions before it starts. This was effected by using a two-horsepower three-cylinder Brotherhood engine worked by high-pressure water and having keyed to its shaft a pulley of compressed paper. This hydraulic engine was levered along guides so as to force the paper pulley against the gas engine flywheel. As soon as the gas engine started the hydraulic motor was withdrawn and the water shut off. Each of the gas engines was fitted with this hydraulic starting gear.

The price for high-pressure water at 800 lb/in² varied from 12s 6d (62½p) per 1000 gallons for a minimum supply of 4000 gallons per quarter to 2s 2d (11p) per thousand for 300000 gallons per quarter, the price for the ordinary city supply at 70 lb/in² being such that using the minimum quantity the high-pressure supply provided 11 times the energy at only 9⅜ times the cost while using 300000 gallons per quarter gave 11 times the energy for only 4⅓ times the cost.

4.7   MELBOURNE HYDRAULIC POWER SUPPLY

On 17 December 1887 the government of the State of Victoria passed 'An Act to facilitate the supply of Motive Power on the High Pressure Hydraulic System for the Extinguishing of Fires and other purposes in Melbourne and its vicinity'. This Act defined the powers of a company already in existence, permitting it to operate for thirty years from a stipulated date after which its assets would become the property of the Local Authority. The commencing date for the thirty year period was finally fixed by an amending act of 24 October 1890 as 1 January 1895.

A company called The Melbourne Hydraulic Power Company Limited had been registered and incorporated as a Joint Stock Company under the Companies Statute Act of the State of Victoria on 24 June 1886.

The company commenced supply in July 1889. It ceased to operate as a public company on 31 December 1924 when it was taken over by the Melbourne City Council in accordance with the Act of 1887. The company had operated profitably up to 1924 and sought an extension of its operating rights by a lease from the City Council for seven years, but this was not granted. Two steam-driven stations were replaced by electrically driven pumps in 1928. The City Council supplied hydraulic power from 1925 to the end of 1967 when high maintenance costs and decreasing revenue resulted in closure of operations.

A pamphlet issued by the company in December 1889 stated that seven miles of mains had been laid from Australian Wharf up Flinders Lane, Little Collins Street, Little Bourke Street to Parliament Houses, parts of King Street, Elizabeth Street, Queen Street, etc., thus embracing nearly the whole of the city. These mains were supplied with water at a pressure of 700 lb/in^2 by the central Pumping Station at Australian Wharf. Two hydraulic accumulators were used. The water supply was taken from the Yarra and passed through a system of filters. The power was available day and night. Greathead fire hydrants were available, the minimum charge for one hydrant being £5 per annum and for one to three £4 per annum. The charge for the first hour's use during a fire was £20 and each hour after £10. Various types of machines were available on deferred payments or hire and the pamphlet listed some 102 consumers. By 1894 the company was supplying power to 413 machines consuming 1 500 000 gallons per week with a total mains length of 18 miles.

No details of the station plant are available. At the time of the reversion of the undertaking to the City Council two pumping stations were mentioned, a No. 1 station owned by the Harbour Trust Commissioners and leased to the company and a No. 2 station on freehold land in Francis Street. Arrangements were made for No. 1 station to be leased to the Council for three years from 1 January 1925. Then the equipment of No. 1 station was listed as

2 main pumping engines.
2 small pumping engines.
2 accumulators.
3 multi-tubular boilers and associated piping.
2 tanks which formed the roof of the engine room.

The company then had 709 customers the equipment being listed as

Hydraulic goods lifts 428
Hydraulic Passenger Lifts 168
Hydraulic Presses 42
Hydraulic Jiggers 14
Hydraulic Hydrants 41
Hydraulic Capstans 6
Hydraulic Cranes 6
Hydraulic Gates 2
Hydraulic Vacuum cleaner 1
Hydraulic Ejector 1

On reversion the hydraulic undertaking became the responsibility of the Electric Supply Committee of the Council and the equipment was ultimately transferred to the Electric Power Station, the then engineer to the Hydraulic Company becoming a consultant under the City Electrical Engineer.

4.8 SYDNEY HYDRAULIC SUPPLY SYSTEM

In 1890 the government of the State of New South Wales passed an Act of Parliament authorizing the setting up of a hydraulic supply system in Sydney. The Sydney Hydraulic Power Company commenced to supply power in January 1891, the company engineer being Mr George Swinburne as in Melbourne. The rate of delivery of power water for the December of that year was 240 000 gallons per week which by May 1894 had become 740 000 gallons per week with some 201 machines connected, these being listed as

Passenger and Goods Lifts	149
Whip Hoists	22
Dumping Presses	7
Cranes	20
Motors	2

The pumping station was situated in Pier Street, Darling Harbour, and it originally consisted of an engine room, boiler house, accumulator tower, coal store, and a large yard for pipe storage etc. (Fig. 4.18).

The engine house contained three sets of horizontal high-pressure steam pumping engines of the Armstrong type (Fig. 4.19), two pairs having cylinders 24 in diameter by 30 in stroke, and one pair cylinders 16 in diameter by 24 in stroke. With a working pressure of 100 lb/in² at the boilers each pair of large engines was capable of delivering 475 gallons per minute at a pressure of 750 lb/in² when running at 50 rev/min while the smaller set of engines was capable of delivering 200 gallons per minute with the same working pressure but running at 60 rev/min.

Each set of engines was complete in itself having two high-pressure cylinders and two directly connected double-acting pumps complete on the one bedplate, the .24-in bore engines having flywheels 11 ft in diameter each weighing 95 cwt, and the 16-in cylinder engines flywheels 9 ft diameter weighing 70 cwt. The steam cylinders were fitted with expansion valves capable of being adjusted while the engines were running. The large engines had pump cylinders 7½ in bore fitted with rams 7½ in

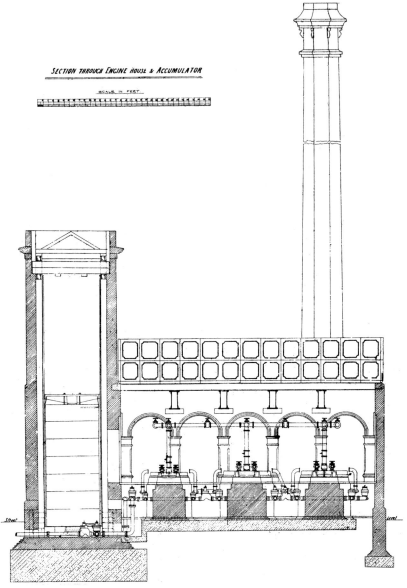

SECTION THROUGH ENGINE HOUSE & ACCUMULATOR

SCALE IN FEET

Fig. 4.18(a) SYDNEY HYDRAULIC POWER STATION
Engine house and accumulator.

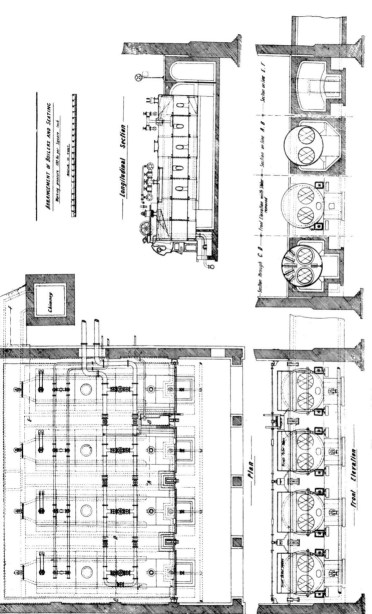

Fig. 4.18(b) SYDNEY HYDRAULIC POWER STATION
Boiler house

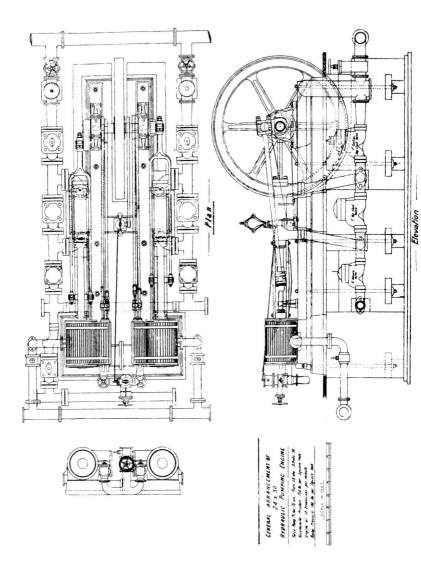

Plan

Elevation

GENERAL ARRANGEMENT OF
24 x 30
HYDRAULIC PUMPING ENGINE

SCALE IN FEET

Fig. 4.19   SYDNEY HYDRAULIC POWER STATION — PUMPING ENGINE

in the piston part and 5⅜ in in the body part, the corresponding dimensions for the smaller set being 5 in and 3⅜ in.

The decision to use twin HP non-condensing instead of compound condensing engines was influenced by the following considerations: the extra first cost of compound engines, the difficulty of obtaining a supply of water for condensing purposes, increased complication and consequent extra cost of maintenance, and at that time Sydney had a cheap coal supply. The economy claimed for compound condensing engines under these conditions was open to question.

The two accumulators had rams 20 in diameter with a stroke of 22 ft, each being loaded with 100 tons of gravel, an extra 5 tons of load being supplied by the weight of the ram and casing. By loading one accumulator slightly heavier than the other they rose successively, the lagging one being the controlling accumulator which actuated a throttle valve in the main pipe so that steam was shut off when the accumulator had nearly reached the topmost part of its travel.

Pipework in general was duplicated so that any section of the system could be isolated to effect repairs.

The boilers were four in number, of the Lancashire type, 7 ft in diameter by 25 ft long, fitted with Hopkinson's dead weight pyramid safety valve and a double lever safety valve, the boilers being fired by Vicars' mechanical stokers.

Two mains left the pumping station and ran in the same line until Sussex Street was reached in Liverpool Street. Here the mains diverged, one following Sussex Street to Market Street where a circuit was formed by the connection of the Sussex Street main with the one in Pitt Street through Market Street (Fig. 4.20). The six-inch main continued through Pitt Street and George Street to meet again at Bridge Street. A six-inch main from Market Street continued through Kent Street to Miller's Point then along Windmill Street to join the Pitt Street main at Circular Quay. Smaller circuits of four- and three-inch mains went around many of the city blocks to connect with the trunk mains at two points. Stop valves were provided at about every 300 yd and at the junctions of all sub mains so that any portion could be isolated as required, thus reducing to a minimum the

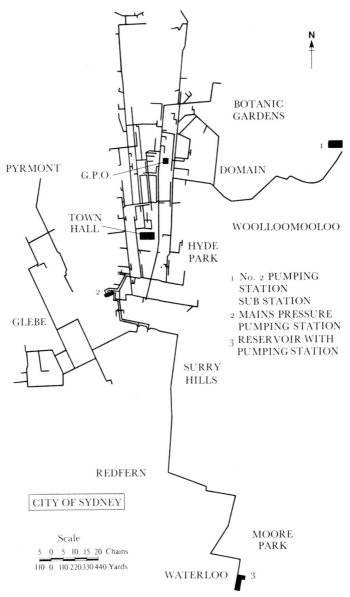

Fig. 4.20   STREET MAP SHOWING SYDNEY HYDRAULIC POWER MAINS

time of stoppage should the fracture of a main occur. Tee pieces for 2 in, 3 in, or 4 in branches were placed at convenient points from which service pipes could be taken to consumers' premises. The mains were placed under the footways, the original intention being to obviate any necessity to disturb the wood-blocking of the streets and this had the advantages of enabling a shorter and cheaper connection to be effected and making repairs much easier to carry out. The mains also extended to the Pyrmont side of Darling Harbour for the operation of cranes. The total length of mains in 1894 was twelve miles and ultimately they extended to twenty miles.

At first water for the power supply was taken from the city water supply system through a six-inch main but the cost of the water proved prohibitive and a cheaper source of supply was sought. A long lease was taken on ten acres of land lying between Mount Rennie and Waterloo at the foot of the sand hills and a dam erected to provide a storage capacity of some 750 000 gallons which was later increased to about 1 000 000 gallons. A pumping station was built to contain a boiler and a set of Worthington compound condensing pumping engines capable of dealing with 25 000 gallons per hour connected to Pier Street by 2½ miles of main, the water being delivered to a tank forming the roof of the engine house and measuring 50 ft × 40 ft × 8 ft deep, the tank being divided into two compartments in one of which the water was allowed to settle before overflowing into the second, from which it passed by a duplicate set of pipes to the pumping engines. This source of supply remained in use until 1965, after which water was obtained from a borehole situated at the foot of the testing tower of Elevators Pty Ltd in Dowling Street, from which some 20 000 gallons of water were pumped per hour.

The water was sold to consumers by meter, the water being generally measured on the exhaust side though high-pressure meters were used in some cases. In 1894 the minimum charge was £3 per quarter for which 5000 gallons were supplied. When the consumption reached 275 000 gallons per quarter the charge was 5s per thousand gallons.

The company achieved a large measure of success. The power supplied was used mainly for the operation of lifts and at the height of its success it was claimed that in Sydney there were examples of hydraulic lifts not equalled elsewhere. The introduction of the hydraulic supply resulted in the discontinuance of many private power installations and it was reported in 1894 that at least some twenty-five gas engines had been supplanted representing a total of some 175 horsepower.

In 1952 the pumping station was electrified, the steam pumping plant being replaced by three electrically driven centrifugal pumps each capable of pumping up to 10 000 gallons per hour at 750 lb/in². After that, however, demand dropped until in 1975 it was of the order of a third of that of twenty years previously. This was due in part to electrical competition and the decrease in the number of hydraulically operated lifts and hoists, ageing of plant, and depreciation of mains on account of age and disturbance due to reconstruction work. Continually rising costs presented a bleak outlook for some time and ultimately the closure of the supply, which took place in June 1975, was inevitable, Sydney predeceasing London by one year.

4.9   ANTWERP LIGHTING SYSTEM

In 1893 the electric lighting of Antwerp* was being established upon a combined hydraulic and electric system. Hydraulic power generated by steam plant was conveyed through pipes to various sub-stations in the city where it was converted by means of water turbines and dynamos into electrical energy for distribution through the network of conductors. Although not completely a hydraulic power system it is worthy of note as evidence of the opinion then held that hydraulic transmission of power was the most efficient method available at that time. Special Pelton wheels were being used in London (see p. 99) for on-site generation of electrical power but there is no reason to believe that the water turbines used at Antwerp were more efficient than the Pelton wheel.

---

* E. B. Ellington. *Proc. Instn. Civ. Engrs.*, Vol. CXV. 1893–94.

CHAPTER FIVE

The Electro-Hydraulic Era

DEVELOPMENTS in the generation and transmission of hydraulic power seem to have reached a measure of finality by the end of the nineteenth century. The reciprocating steam engine offered simplicity and reliability. The reciprocating plunger pump possessed similar virtues and the two were united in the triple expansion units which became almost standard and which for size and characteristics admirably met the requirements of the early public hydraulic power stations enabling them to meet satisfactorily the nature and extent of the demands made upon them. The d.c. electric stations of the period, due to transmission problems were only capable of meeting the needs of a small area and consequently were small in size. There was a large and increasing demand for hydraulic power by dock and railway companies but in these cases circumstances made it desirable for such concerns to have their own power supply stations. The small early electric stations were mainly concerned with the lighting load so the only alternative to a piped hydraulic power supply was small steam or gas engines on the consumer's premises and the advantages of hydraulic supply for lifts, cranes, presses, and the driving of small machinery were obvious. Consequently the progress of the public hydraulic companies after a very promising start was plodding and uneventful with a steady increase in demand over roughly the next two and a half decades.

However, in collateral fields over the same period a very different state of affairs prevailed. In the electricity supply industry, from 1882 to 1900 many new power stations were built though these did not conform to any particular pattern; in fact they were very diverse in character. There were in 1894, power stations at Newcastle, Cambridge, and Scarborough with no other prime movers than steam turbines and this at a time when there were other stations still using small vertical and horizontal reciprocating engines driving dynamos through belts or ropes. Towards the end of the century alternators were being designed to be direct coupled to horizontal slow-speed engines.

In general, up to about 1904, the reciprocating steam engine held the field, the ultimate in high-speed engine design being represented by the Willans and Bellis totally enclosed vertical engines direct coupled to generators. The Willans engine, Fig. 5.1, was first patented in 1884. It had tandem cylinders, single acting, the steam being distributed by a piston valve working in a hollow piston rod. It was built in a number of sizes as simple, compound,

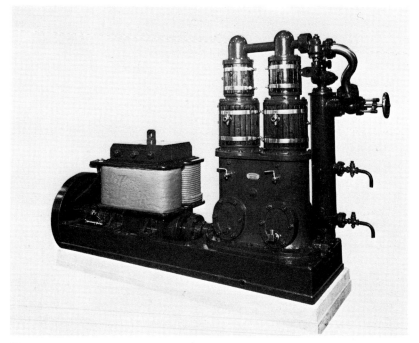

Fig. 5.1   WILLANS TWO-CRANK COMPOUND CENTRAL VALVE ENGINE AND DYNAMO
c. 1888
The engine developed 18 horsepower at 450 rev/min. Courtesy Science Museum.

or triple expansion, with one, two, or three cranks, and finally four triple-expansion three-crank engines of 2500 horsepower were constructed. Three of these were installed in the Upper Boat Power Station of the South Wales Electric Power Company (see p. 150).

The rapid growth of the electrical supply industry at the turn of the century is shown by the following table of the number of supply undertakings in the United Kingdom:

Year	Companies	Municipalities
1898	70	93
1903	157	213
1908	203	338

But up to about 1898 the main demand was for electricity for lighting. After that the demand for electrical energy for power purposes increased rapidly as is illustrated by the following table relating to the Glasgow Electricity Supply, based on figures given in the *Glasgow Herald* 14 December 1909.

Year	Lighting h.p.	Power h.p.	Total h.p.	$\dfrac{\text{Power h.p.}}{\text{Total h.p.}}$ %
1898	7899	301	8200	3·67
1900	13806	1894	15700	12·06
1902	22407	4593	27000	17·01
1904	32634	9366	42000	22·30
1906	36695	19805	56500	35·05
1908	36495	29505	66000	44·70

It is important to note that it was not until the beginning of the present century that the electricity stations became serious competitors in the power supply field.

While the advantages of high-voltage transmission were appreciated, opinion was sharply divided on the choice of a.c. or d.c. and the 'battle of the systems' proceeded for many years with eminent protagonists on both sides. Direct current had the advantage that accumulators could be used to meet the off-peak lighting load either at the station or on consumers' premises, but the stepping up of the voltage for transmission purposes and stepping down at the other end were not easy, involving rotary converters in the case of d.c. instead of the simpler static transformer in the case of a.c. Also generation at high voltages was more difficult in the case of d.c. Nevertheless a number of early d.c. stations used transmission voltages of the order of 2000.

The development of the tramcar, first introduced in 1891, helped considerably to increase the demand for electric power and gave an impetus to the development of the d.c. motor. A disadvantage of a.c. systems was that with the single-phase systems then popular the a.c. motor was inferior to its d.c. counterpart. Each early alternator had to have its own separate system until the problem of the parallel working of alternators was solved. Ultimately, with the introduction of three-phase systems and the discovery by Ferraris in 1885 of the principle of the induction motor these problems disappeared while the static transformer provided the immediate key to the solution of transmission problems.

The advantages of the steam turbine over the reciprocating engine were becoming obvious. It was capable of using much higher steam pressures, could expand steam down to lower pressures, thus becoming more thermally efficient, and its bulk did not increase disproportionately to the increase in power output. Although the steam turbine was not without its teething troubles, by the turn of the century the Parsons turbo-generator was being built in units of 500 kW capacity, and the reciprocating engine which had long been the pride and joy of the mechanical engineer had soon to start the fight for its very existence. The fight was to be a long one, sustained by improvements in valve gears, the invention of the uniflow engine, and the building of large units with very impressive performance, but ultimately the turbine triumphed. By 1907 a turbine of 7000 kW capacity had been built, by 1919 turbines of 25 000 kW were available, and by 1933 a capacity of 100 000 kW had been reached, by which time the battle had been well and truly lost.

Boilermakers were quick to meet the challenge and large water-tube boilers capable of steaming at the much higher pressures soon made the old fire-tube boilers obsolete except for very small powers.

Improvements in alternators and the rapid development of the steam turbine made electric power a sound economic proposition and the resultant big increase in demand paved the way for the large central stations and ultimately the grid system and brought about the demise of the local electricity supply companies and the municipal stations. With stations linked together by the grid the consequences of a breakdown could be minimized and large power units exploited to their maximum advantage thus reducing generating costs, while high-voltage transmission at 132 000 volts drastically reduced transmission losses, and electricity became available to consumers at a standard supply voltage and frequency all over the country.

The general availability of electric power had a profound effect on factory layout. No longer was power distributed to machines by countershaft and belt but integral drives became universal. Integral individual drives had become possible by, and were an attractive advantage of, hydraulic power, but hydraulic supplies were limited to a few localities so the design and manufacture of machines with inbuilt hydraulic drives would have had a very limited appeal and was not at the time a commercial proposition. But because they met special needs the immediate impact on the public hydraulic stations of these developments was small: they continued to plod along supplying local power requirements, in general where linear and not rotary motion was required, i.e., for lifts, hoists, cranes, presses, in particular, and in some cases swing and bascule bridges, as well as a variety of injector pumps, and water for fire fighting using the special injectors. So hydraulic power held its own in these fields for many years and even after electric power became more economic hydraulic supplies continued to be used on account of their special suitability for specific purposes and the fact that the mains supply was available. But the continuing rapid strides in electrical power generation and transmission presented the hydraulic stations with formidable opposition and limited their expansion.

It should not be concluded that the success of the steam turbine was ignored by the hydraulic engineer. Turbine-driven centrifugal pumps of quite large sizes were manufactured, principally for dock installations. Only an isolated example of the use of such a unit is recorded, that being the unit installed at the Wapping Station of the London Hydraulic Power Company in 1926 (see p. 110).

The development in generating units was not the main reason for the triumph of the electric stations. To make use of bigger generating plant it is necessary to have a bigger demand and this means either an increase in the operating area or an increase in the intensity of demand – to which there will be a definite limit. Increasing the area of operation involves greater distances of transmission. If transmission distances are increased then, to maintain the same efficiency of transmission, it will be necessary to increase the supply pressure in the case of hydraulic stations or the supply voltage in the case of electric stations.

Transmission at high voltages presents little difficulty compared with transmission of high water pressure and this is the one, and the vital point, on which the superiority of electricity must be conceded. The basic difficulty is the fundamental difference in the two media concerned. High-voltage electricity can be carried by a wire the size of which depends only on the amperage or rate of flow, and very high voltages and powers can be efficiently transmitted with relatively outstanding cheapness, by overhead wires. But high-pressure water calls for thick and expensive pipes the internal diameter of which depends on the rate of flow, and the thickness of the pipe wall on the water pressure.

Such were the developments and difficulties which halted the progress of public piped hydraulic power, and forced the hydraulic power concerns either to change their policy or face lingering stagnation. Thus started the twilight of what may be regarded as the first hydraulic era in the saga of public power transmission and distribution.

It was obvious by the mid 1920s that for the transmission of power over long distances electricity had no rival. But there were many operations for which hydraulic power had outstanding inherent advantages, that is the fields of distribution and utilization still offered scope for hydraulic power.

The necessity for the re-assessment of the policy of the hydraulic power stations arose from the levelling off, followed by a fall, of demand. By this time not only had electric power become very competitive in price but labour costs, with course of time, had increased and electrical operation offered the big advantage of automatic or semi-automatic control whereas the existing steam power stations were very labour-intensive. The choice was between electrification and slow decline and ultimate closure. The two largest concerns, London and Manchester, stood to benefit most, and were the first to convert, followed by Glasgow, and Liverpool very much later. Hull and Sydney retained their original character to the bitter end. The details of the changes have already been given in the accounts of the various stations in Chapter 4. It is sufficient to observe here that with electrification the hydraulic power stations changed their character, virtually becoming trans-former sub-stations converting electrical to hydraulic power for a group of users interested in processes for which hydraulic operation offered outstanding advantages while taking advantage of the fact that the mains were available and thus no capital outlay in this direction was called for.

A further entirely separate development dealt a serious blow to the hydraulic power companies but proved a boon to manu-facturers of hydraulic equipment and opened a new and more promising era in the history of hydraulic power. The positive rotary pump has a long history and much ingenuity had been displayed in its development and this was supplemented by the fact that towards the end of the nineteenth century much attention was being paid to the rotary engine, but efforts in this direction went conspicuously unrewarded. However, a number of mechanisms devised as potential engines when driven in reverse became efficient pumps, so a wide range of designs was available. Most were compact, robust, able to give high output pressures with continuous flow and capable of running at high speeds. They were awaiting a power unit capable of exploiting their qualities and this came with the development of the a.c. motor.

Some positive rotary pumps are of the variable capacity type, that is, their output can be varied independently of the speed while the pump is running, and hence they can give a variable output when coupled to a constant speed motor.

The small rotary pump offered greater versatility. Being small and compact it could be installed on the consumer's premises as a unit with integral electric drive, or even built into a machine. It was now possible for each machine to have its own hydraulic supply, a point of importance where different working pressures are desirable. Such pump units are today available for normal working pressures of up to 1000 lb/in² though 5000 lb/in² is possible for special cases, and they permit the use of a hydraulic fluid other than water. Water freezes in cold weather and is highly corrosive. The use of an oil overcomes these objections and solves lubrication problems.

Unit hydraulic systems offer greater versatility and efficiency and their introduction led to the more extensive use of hydraulic apparatus particularly in metal working, metal testing, plastics, and machine tools not to mention the specialist applications in automobile and aircraft engineering which go beyond the scope of this book.

The hydraulic press has, since its invention, been a very versatile tool but in some fields, e.g., metal drawing and stamping, it was too slow and ponderous to compete with other forms such as the crank and toggle press. Thanks to the individual pump unit the modern high-speed hydraulic press has established production records while it has found a new field of application in synthetic plastics.

Hydraulic power is now very widely used in the field of machine tools for obtaining a wide variety of movements from shaping, planing, and slotting to hydraulic copying.

The use of oil as the working fluid obviously does not permit of allowing the exhaust to flow to waste as when water was used. Consequently there evolved the self-contained hydraulic power pack consisting of pump, instruments, return flow system, filters, etc., ready to be coupled to a suitable motor.

Many positive rotary pumps can be worked in reverse, that is when supplied with fluid under pressure they become efficient motors and variable-capacity pumps become in effect, variable-speed motors. So the hydraulic power pack can be used to provide a very efficient variable speed drive offering unique advantages over reduction gears, and this field provides considerable promise for the future.

Though it provides the only answer where a small number of

items of equipment are concerned, the thinking behind the hydraulic power pack has been largely defensive – a desire for hydraulics to hold its own. More positive thinking has led to the concept of the centralized hydraulic power system which involves electrical transmission combined with hydraulic distribution, its supporters maintaining that with the proper approach and encouragement from manufacturers hydraulic distribution could offer advantages over, and compete successfully with, electrical distribution in many fields.

With unit hydraulic power packs each piece of equipment will be driven by its own motor and will have its own instrumentation, filters, etc., which will call for periodical inspection and maintenance. The motor will run continuously while the unit is in use regardless of the load on the pump it drives. In the case of a number of such units not all will be working to capacity all the time. Appreciable economy could be effected by having a central pumping plant to supply a number of units and due to the diversification of the load the maximum load at any one time will be less than the sum of the individual maximum loads. Thus capital, running, and maintenance costs could be reduced. Provided an adequate selection of hydraulic equipment suited to the needs of the user is available, e.g., a wide range of hydraulic motor sizes and types, such systems could compete successfully with electrical distribution, and as they became more generally adopted there would be an increasing incentive to manufacturers to improve the scope, size, and versatility of the plant available. Advocates of centralized hydraulic systems compare the development of the electrical supply industry at the turn of the century with the state of affairs in the hydraulic equipment industry today and argue that 'on economic and technical grounds hydraulic motors should supersede electric motors just as electric motors displaced line shafting'. The rapid strides in the adoption of the electric drive were due to close cooperation between motor manufacturers and users and free and frank discussions of the problems involved. It has further been contended that 'the oil hydraulics industry now may be regarded as being in a comparable position to the electrical engineering industry at the beginning of the century. The technology is well established, but is not yet a normal part of engineering education; nor is it being projected by hydraulics manufacturers to users'.*

The conclusion appears to be that if the manufacturers of hydraulic equipment follow the example of the electrical industry we shall shortly enter a new Hydraulic Age. The passing of the public hydraulic power stations has not marked the end of hydraulic distribution of power but rather the beginning of a new approach to it based on new technology and the experience of the past.

THEN AND NOW

The following are brief details of two electricity generating stations, one built at the turn of the century, the other, one of the latest super power stations.

South Wales Electric Power Co, Upper Boat Station, Treforest

This station was one of the first of the regional stations, representing a departure from the small d.c. district stations, and the fore-runners of the central stations. It was intended to supply the needs of South Wales outside the larger towns which had their own stations. It was also amongst the last of the reciprocating engine stations to be built.

Building started in 1902 and the three 2500 h.p. Willans engines were operational in April 1904. One of the engines is shown in Fig. 5.2, direct coupled to an alternator of 1500 kW output, the generating voltage, and the transmission voltage being 11000 volts. At that time no British firm could meet the requirements, so the alternators were made in Budapest.

A general idea of size may be obtained from the fact that the station electrical engineer, standing in front of one of the LP cylinders was 5 ft 6 in (1·69 m) in height. The overall length of the engine and alternator was about 30 ft (9·14 m) and the height about 20 ft (6·1 m). The steam pressure was 180 lb/in² and the engine was condensing, having an air pump of the Edwards type.

---

* 'The evaluation of existing hydraulic equipment for use in industrial power systems' by B. C. Wilkins – *Hydraulic & Air Engineering*, April/May 1977.

Fig. 5.2   TRIPLE EXPANSION WILLANS ENGINE OF 2500 H.P. AT UPPER BOAT POWER
STATION, TREFOREST

The speed of the set was 150 rev/min. No turning engine (to get the cranks into starting position), normal with engines of this size, was fitted, and the engine had to be 'barred' around by lever and ratchet mechanism needing several men to operate it. The first turbo-alternator, a 3000 kW set, was installed in August 1908 after which the engines were only used for standby purposes, and by 1920 they were out of service. The first was scrapped in 1921 and the other two in 1936 to make way for turbine sets. An 18 MW (18 000 kW) set was installed in 1923 and by 1942 the station capacity was 153 MW made up of three 30 MW sets and one each of 25, 20, and 18 MW capacity. The station was closed in 1966 and the building was demolished later.

For details of the generating plant and Fig. 5.2 the author is indebted to Mr H. T. Williams who was employed at the station for 42 years. The author also has nostalgic memories since as an apprentice attending Barry Evening Classes in the early twenties he participated in an organized visit to the station to obtain some idea of contemporary power station practice.

An indication of the progress made this century will be obtained from the following brief details of one of the most recent stations built by the Central Electricity Generating Board at Eggborough, near Goole, and officially opened in 1970.

Eggborough Power Station
Eggborough is one of the large 2000 MW stations built near the Yorkshire coalfield to exploit the ready availability of large quantities of coal. The site area is some 400 acres (160 hectares) close to the River Aire, from which the cooling water make-up is taken.

The generating plant consists of four turbo-alternators each with an output of 500 000 kW (500 MW) and each is coupled to a single pulverized-fuel boiler. In addition there are four standby gas turbine generators each of 17·5 MW capacity. The steam pressure at the turbine stop valve is 2300 lb/in^2 gauge, temperature 568°C. The turbine speed is 3000 rev/min, the terminal voltage 22 000, and each turbo-alternator is about 165 ft (50·29 m) long. The electricity generated is fed into the national grid at 400 kV. The station coal consumption is 19 200 tons per day (max.) of small coal unfit for domestic use. Construction began in 1962 and the station first supplied electricity to the grid in 1967.

While it may be argued that much of the spectacular progress in electrical generation and transmission has been due to a change of 'working fluid' from low-voltage d.c. to extra-high-voltage three-phase a.c. in much the same way as the scope of hydraulic distribution has been increased by the change from relatively low-pressure water to high-pressure oil, it would indeed be a wild dream that envisaged hydraulic generation and transmission of power on the same scale. But, as we have seen, hydraulic distribution has much to offer and the future may yet see the opponents of the past settling down to a mutually profitable co-existence each finding much to be proud of in the story of its past.

Appendix

A.1 COMPARATIVE COSTS OF HYDRAULIC AND ELECTRIC POWER

For details of costs we are dependent upon the literature of the period and this naturally gives costs in terms of the units then in use. The literature is particularly fascinating in the light it throws on the attitudes and thinking of the time. It is hoped that the reader will be prompted to consult these sources for himself and with this possibility in mind costs and quantities in the first instance are direct quotes with the modern equivalents in brackets, and the source identified. Checking and any further comparisons that may be necessary will be facilitated by the use of the table of conversion factors on p. 166.

It must in the first instance be pointed out that switchboard or station costs, while useful as bases of comparison of generating costs, do not include transmission and other costs, e.g., mains upkeep, interest charges, depreciation, and rates and taxes, and are not the cost to the consumer.

E. B. Ellington, in a paper read before the Glasgow meeting of the Institution of Mechanical Engineers in 1895 made a comparison of the costs of producing hydraulic and electric power based on information in the records of the London Hydraulic Power Company and the Westminster Electric Supply Corporation for the year 1894. The cost of hydraulic power was 5·172d per 1000 gallons that is, 0·474p per 1000 litres, and in terms of kilowatt-hours the costs were 0·3304p for hydraulic power and 0·5762p for electric power.

The difference in cost was put in another way by Professor

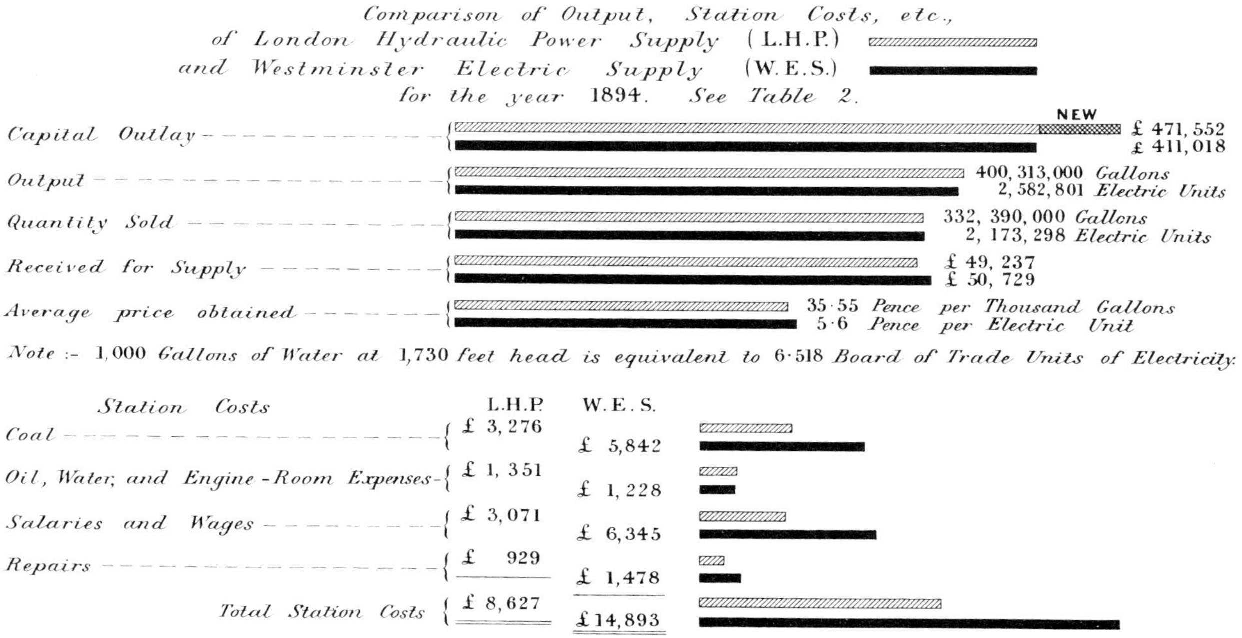

Comparison of Output, Station Costs, etc.,
of London Hydraulic Power Supply (L.H.P.)
and Westminster Electric Supply (W.E.S.)
for the year 1894. See Table 2.

NEW

Capital Outlay
£ 471, 552
£ 411, 018

Output
400, 313,000 Gallons
2, 582, 801 Electric Units

Quantity Sold
332, 390, 000 Gallons
2, 173, 298 Electric Units

Received for Supply
£ 49, 237
£ 50, 729

Average price obtained
35·55 Pence per Thousand Gallons
5·6 Pence per Electric Unit

Note :— 1,000 Gallons of Water at 1,730 feet head is equivalent to 6·518 Board of Trade Units of Electricity.

Station Costs	L.H.P.	W.E.S.
Coal	£ 3, 276	£ 5, 842
Oil, Water, and Engine-Room Expenses	£ 1, 351	£ 1, 228
Salaries and Wages	£ 3, 071	£ 6, 345
Repairs	£ 929	£ 1, 478
Total Station Costs	£ 8, 627	£ 14, 893

Fig. A.1   RELATIVE COSTS OF HYDRAULIC AND ELECTRIC POWER 1894

W. H. Watkinson.* 'With practically the same capital outlay the comparative station costs were, coal cost 80 per cent more with electrical generation, salaries and wages amounted to 108 per cent more, and repairs and maintenance 60 to 114 per cent more.'

The position was explained in part by the facts that electric generators when not running at full load ran at full speed, but with hydraulic power the speed of the engines practically altered with the demand since the hydraulic pumping engines were automatically controlled by the accumulator, and regulated their speed to suit the output, so avoiding both unnecessary wear and tear and the reduction of mechanical efficiency which takes place when engines not fully loaded have to run at constant speed; and also in general, maintenance costs of hydraulic plant are relatively low. At the time, the demand for power other than that for tramway or railway work, was of an intermittent character and the system of small generating units adopted at hydraulic power stations was one which lent itself to the most economical generation of power in the circumstances.

By the late 1880s specially designed Pelton wheels direct coupled to electric generators were replacing the hydraulic engines hitherto used and enabled 66 per cent of the hydraulic energy to be utilized as electric energy. Taking the cost of hydraulic power supplied as 2s (10p) per 1000 gallons the cost of the electrical energy obtained in this way worked out at about 6d (2½p) per kilowatt-hour and was competitive with the prevailing lighting rate, and developments in this direction were anticipated, though in 1893 Ellington admitted that 'since 1887 there have been few new important applications of hydraulic power'.

While, as we have seen, the period 1894 to the end of the century was one of steady prosperity for the hydraulic supply industry, on the electrical supply side it was one of very rapid development. Stations ceased to be small catering mainly for a lighting load, and increasing power load and particularly tramway load improved the load factor and helped to decrease unit costs. By 1903 switchboard costs of 0·34d and 0·35d (0·1458p) were reported (at the discussion

---

* 'F. J. Haswell on Hydraulic Machinery', *Liverpool Engineering Society Transactions.* 1903, Vol. XXIV, p. 110.

on Haswell's paper) but these were regarded as exceptional. Nevertheless by then a number of towns were offering electricity for power purposes at 1½d (0·6p) per unit while Wigan charged 1d (0·4p) per unit. At the Wapping station of the London Hydraulic Power Co the station cost, not including interest and depreciation, for the year 1900 came out at 0·1937p per kilowatt-hour.

Separate charges were made for electricity used for light and power and this practice persisted until well into the 1930s, the charge for electricity used for lighting being several times that for power, and the costs issue is somewhat blurred by concessionary rates to large power users and multi-part tariffs which became common. Also with very rapid increase in the number and size of stations the cost of producing electricity varied appreciably from place to place, and time to time.

The 1914–18 war provided a big boost for the electricity supply industry but had little effect on hydraulic supplies. The production of war material made unprecedented demands for electric power and exposed defects in legislation under which isolated development was fostered. The desirability of the interconnection of generating stations was highlighted and a special department was formed to organize the supply of electric power.

The immediate post-war years were periods of depression and industrial unrest not conducive to expansion, but many new stations were built, the maximum capacity being 100000 kW.

In 1927 the number of supply undertakings with distribution rights was 623 and these possessed 491 generating stations with a total output for the year 1927–8 of 8550000000 units, excluding railway, tramway, and non-statutory undertakings. The government then decided to introduce legislation establishing the Central Electricity Board, the function of which was to develop a national super-power system and it was estimated that by 1940–41 the large industrial manufacturers would be able to obtain electricity at ½d (0·2p) per unit while the national average for all supplies would be 1d per unit.

The hostilities of 1939–45 which intervened were kind to the electricity supply industry but as we have seen unkind to the hydraulic supply companies. Although the post-war promise of electricity for all at ½d per unit was not realized, increasing costs hit all industries alike and it was all too apparent that the hydraulic supply industry, saddled with ageing plant, could not possibly compete in the generating field and that survival lay in electrification, cutting of operational costs, and the transmission of energy in a form which had its own peculiar advantages.

The price of hydraulic energy to the consumer varied considerably from place to place and time to time. The following brief summary will provide an overall picture of the relative state of affairs at the most interesting periods. Costs per 1000 gallons are not directly comparable as allowance must be made for the differences in supply pressure. This, of course, is implicit in the calculations of costs per kilowatt-hour.

In 1895 the London Hydraulic Power Co was supplying some seven million gallons of water per week at an average cost of 3s per 1000 gallons (2·30p per kilowatt-hour). The rate for 500 000 gallons per quarter was 2s per 1000 gallons (1·53p per kWh). For motors running regularly for several hours per day a special rate of 1s 6d per 1000 gallons (1·15p per kWh) applied and Ellington claimed that 'it is questionable whether power can by any means be obtained at a lower rate when all the items of cost have been taken into account'.

At Liverpool in 1903 the charges for power for lifting, pressing, and intermittent work were on a scale from £1 for 2000 gallons (15·3p per kWh) to £42 10s 0d for 300 000 gallons (2·18 per kWh). A guaranteed minimum of 500 000 gallons was charged at 2s per 1000 (1·53p per kWh) with a million gallons charged at 1s 6d per 1000 (1·15p per kWh). A special rate which worked out at 3d (1·25p) to 4d (1·66p) according to the quantity used, was charged for rotary motors running several hours daily.

The charges at Glasgow in the year 1932–3 were 2000 gallons £1 7s 6d (14.17p per kWh), 10 000 gallons £5 7s 3d (5.54p per kWh) and 100 000 gallons £19 2s 6d (1·91p per kWh) with a minimum quarterly charge of £1 7s 6d (£1·37) for one machine up to £8 16s 0d (£8·80) for ten machines.

At Birmingham in 1893 the minimum charge was for a consumption of 4000 gallons at 12s 6d per 1000 (9·02p per kWh) while for a quarterly consumption of 300 000 gallons the charge was 2s 2d per 1000 (1·56p per kWh). The cost of the ordinary city water supply at a pressure of 70 lb/in^2 was 1s 4d per 1000 gallons and a selling point was made of the fact that at the minimum consumption charge of 12s 6d per 1000 the high-pressure supply gave 11 times the energy for 9⅜ times the cost.

In Manchester during the later years of the supply, i.e., 1964 to 1971 the charges ranged from 90p per 1000 gallons (9·27p per kWh) to 40p per 1000 gallons (4·12p per kWh) according to consumption, but charges were increased by 25 per cent in 1971 until the closure of the supply in 1972.

In Melbourne in 1889 the minimum quarterly charge was £2 10s 0d per machine with consumptions between 3000 and 10000 gallons charged at 12s 6d per 1000 decreasing to 5s per 1000 gallons for consumptions between 300000 and 400000 gallons, while in Sydney in 1894 the minimum charge was £3 per quarter for which 5000 gallons were supplied, and when the consumption reached 275000 gallons per quarter the charge was 5s per 1000 gallons.

There is almost a complete lack of records of the activities of the Hull Hydraulic Power Company after its inauguration. Hull Corporation was a customer of the company, using hydraulic power for the operation of bridges across the River Hull and for six fire hydrants in High Street, but no records of costs are available. The booklet *The Port of Hull and its facilities for trade* for 1906 refers to a 'large number of wharves and warehouses' using hydraulic power, and oil and cake works had installed sprinkler systems for fire fighting. Excavations in the old town area have revealed a number of 2-in service pipes to consumers' premises but there exists no indication of the use to which the power was put.

The Hull Dock Company in 1876 took a 4-in branch off the power main to work cranes and appliances on the south side of the Queens Dock for which it paid 4s per 1000 gallons of water, with a minimum charge of £200 per annum for the first fifteen connections and a further charge of £15 per annum for each connection above that number.

At its inauguration the hydraulic company issued the following proposed tariff:

1 crane in one warehouse   £50 per annum
2 cranes in one warehouse   £94 per annum
3 cranes in one warehouse   £132 per annum
4 cranes in one warehouse   £166 per annum.

Each crane would have a counter attached to it which would register the work done. The above charges were for up to 4000 foot-tons of work each day by each crane, extra work being charged for at the rate of 4s for every additional 4000 foot-tons. It was stated that special rates would be charged for working presses, hydraulic engines, capstans etc., 'as occasion arises'.

A.2   ALTERNATIVE POWER SOURCES

The rotative beam engine dates from 1780 but these engines were large and cumbersome. One of the earliest of the more compact direct-acting vertical steam engines was Maudslay's table engine, patented in 1807, and in the words of R. J. Law (*The Steam Engine*, a Science Museum Booklet) 'For fifty years it was in favour for such duties as driving workshops'. The modern form of vertical steam engine, the 'inverted' vertical, with the cylinder above the crankshaft, was introduced by James Nasmyth about 1850. Ultimately many types and sizes were available to meet most needs.

The hot-air engine was first introduced by Sir George Cayley in 1807 but the more spectacular efforts were those of Ericsson 1826, and Stirling 1827 and 1840. In general such engines have been very disappointing in their performance though in the small sizes they have made up for in convenience in use what they lacked in efficiency. From about 1850 onwards the Manchester firm of A. & E. Robinson supplied a range of small coal- and gas-fired hot-air engines. The coal-fired engines were used for such purposes as country house pumping plant, and the smaller gas-heated units for purposes for which we now use fractional horsepower electric motors.

As we have seen, the Lenoir gas engine enjoyed a measure of short-lived popularity, but it soon became apparent that it was no rival for the steam engine. It was not until the introduction of the Otto 'Silent' gas engine in 1876, the same year that the Hull Hydraulic Power Co became operational, that the generation of power by gas in competition with the steam engine became a practical proposition.

So for the first three-quarters of the nineteenth century the predominant source of power was the steam engine, wind and water power, except in isolated instances, being confined to flour milling and seed crushing in stamper mills.

The fourth quarter saw the dawn of power transmission over distances, with hydraulic power well in the lead offering cheap power free from all fire risk, and it maintained its lead almost to the turn of the century when competition from the electric stations became intense.

The extent to which gas was a competitor of hydraulic power during this period is somewhat nebulous, deciding factors being no doubt availability, and the cost of gas, which varied appreciably from place to place, depending, among other things, on the size of the gas undertaking and the local price of coal which in turn depended upon the cost of transport.

Most large towns had more than one gas undertaking. In Hull, for example, the town was served by the British Gas Light and Coke Co and the East Hull Gas Co, and the price of gas in the centre of the town in the mid 1870s was 2s 6d (12½p) per 1000 cubic feet. The outskirts were served by smaller companies and about the same time the Sutton, Southcoates and Drypool Gas Light and Coke Co regretted that, being a small company, it could not compete in price with the British Gas Light and Coke Co, though it obtained 'bright clean coal' at 10s 6d (52½p) per ton. The price of gas in Lincoln in 1873 was quoted as 4s 6d (22½p) per 1000 cubic feet with coal at 16s (80p) per ton.

The calorific value of the 'lighting gas' of the period varied from 580 to 813 British Thermal Units per cubic foot.

By 1880 the demand for small gas engines must have been fairly large for a number of firms were engaged in their manufacture. The output of the smaller engines was rated in 'manpower' and some idea of their cost may be obtained from the following advertisement by a firm of gas engine manufacturers in 1884:

'1 man' £22 10s (£22·50), '2 man' £32 10s (£32·50), '3 man' £38 10s (£38.50), ½ h.p. £45, 1 h.p. £55, 2 h.p. £75.

No indication was given of the use to which they were put. The following table, taken from *Calvert's Mechanics' Almanack* for 1895 gives what was claimed to be a fair comparison between gas and steam calculated on a working day of ten hours and including interest on capital and all working expenses:

Comparative cost of small Gas and Steam Engines per Horse Power per Hour

GAS ENGINES

Gas (per 1000 cubic feet). s. d.		½ h.p. d.	1 h.p. d.	2 h.p. d.	3 h.p. d.	4 h.p. d.	6 h.p. d.
3	4	..	4·08	2·64	2·28	2·04	1·92	1·80
2	10	..	3·72	2·40	2·04	1·80	1·68	1·56
2	6	..	3·52	2·26	1·90	1·66	1·55	1·43
2	3	..	3·37	2·15	1·79	1·55	1·46	1·34
2	0	..	3·23	2·05	1·69	1·45	1·37	1·25
1	9	..	3·08	1·94	1·58	1·34	1·27	1·15
1	6	..	2·93	1·84	1·48	1·24	1·18	1·06
1	3	..	2·78	1·73	1·37	1·13	1·08	·96
1	0	..	2·64	1·62	1·26	1·02	·99	·87
	9	..	2·49	1·52	1·16	·92	·89	·77

STEAM ENGINES

Coal (per ton).							
12	6	..	—	2·88	2·04	1·68	1·44	1·32

1s = 5p = 12d

A.3   THE HYDRAULIC ENGINEERING COMPANY LTD, CHESTER

This company was responsible for the manufacture of practically all the hydraulic equipment supplied to the various public supply companies in Britain, and this was largely due to the influence of Mr E. B. Ellington who was President of the Institution of Mechanical Engineers, 1911 to 1912.

A small general engineering business on part of the present site was started by Cole, Whittle & Co in 1803, making small horizontal steam engines and undertaking general millwrighting. It continued until 1832 when John Johnson entered the business. In 1844 the business passed to his sons Edward and Bryan Johnson and during their partnership the engineering side was developed. In 1869, Mr Edward Johnson having retired, Mr E. B. Ellington joined Mr Bryan Johnson in partnership and the business continued under the name of Johnson & Ellington until 1874 when it was made a limited liability company and acquired its present title.

With the introduction of the hydraulic accumulator in 1850 there followed a rapid development in high-pressure hydraulic machinery and Mr Ellington became a prominent pioneer in this field. He designed and produced a considerable amount of hydraulic machinery working at pressures of 700 to 1500 lb/in² (50 to 105 kg/cm²).

The early steam pumping engines were horizontal but the final form was the vertical marine type triple expansion engine which gave the best overall efficiency at that time.

The 1914–18 war effected a fundamental change in outlook regarding electricity supply and the company would have been in serious difficulty but for a heavy demand for hydraulic presses and associated equipment for shell manufacture.

After the first world war a short small boom was followed by a depression but the company managed to keep going on orders for coal hoists and a special machine for laying pipes underground (known as a 'thrust borer') but the number of employees was drastically reduced during the difficult years 1925–35.

The commencement of the second world war in 1939 saw the start of a big demand for hydraulic presses for shell manufacture and business increased so much that by the end of 1941 the order book had to be closed.

During the war period a big change took place in press design. The use of water as the working fluid at pressures of the order of 700 to 1500 lb/in² (50 to 105 kg/cm²) with slow-running pumps and large storage accumulators supplying power to a battery of presses was superseded by individual presses using oil as the working medium at pressures up to 3 tons/in² (472 kg/cm²) from a high-speed pump direct coupled to an electric motor.

Today the company specializes in the manufacture of purpose-built hydraulic presses.

A.4 GRIMSBY WATER TOWER

The purpose of the tower was to supply water under pressure for the operation of cranes and other dock machinery. The first hydraulic crane was erected by Sir W. G. Armstrong (later Lord Armstrong) at the upper end of Newcastle Quay in 1846. Soon afterwards he installed similar cranes at Liverpool. At both places the supply of pressure water was taken from the town mains but the variation in pressure due to the fluctuations in demand proved a disadvantage. The supply pressure in such cases would be in the region of 70 to 90 lb/in^2 corresponding to heads of the order of 160 to 200 ft of water.

When the use of hydraulic power for the operation of dock machinery at the proposed new docks at Great Grimsby was discussed in 1849 it was proposed to install a tank upon a tower supplied by its own source of power which would be free from. outside interference. The result was Grimsby Dock Water Tower, today the tallest landmark in Lincolnshire, which can also be considered a landmark in the history of hydraulic engineering since it formed part of the first independent water supply system laid down primarily for the distribution of water power for the operation of mechanical appliances.

The tower formed part of the Royal Dock scheme, work on which started in 1849, and in addition to supplying water under pressure for the working of the lock gates and dock cranes it also provided a water supply for shipping and dwelling houses on dock premises. The tower was built in brick to support a wrought-iron tank holding 33 000 gallons of water at a height of 200 ft on projecting corbelling (Fig. A.2). The tower is 28 ft square at the base, tapering to 26 ft below the first projection, the walls being 4 ft thick at the base and 3 ft thick below the corbells. The supply water was obtained from a well 25 ft diameter and 47 ft deep with a centre boring of 5 in diameter to the chalk below. The water was pumped up to the tank by duplicate pumps of 10 in bore driven by steam engines. The delivery main supplying pressure water to the locks, etc., was a cast iron pipe 13 in diameter. The pumping machinery was ordered in 1849 but due to delay in the construction of the dock it was not operational until 1851. Some time between 1884 and 1896 the steam pumping plant was replaced by electrically driven pumps.

As mentioned on p. 3, Lord Armstrong when designing the hydraulic system at New Holland considered building a storage

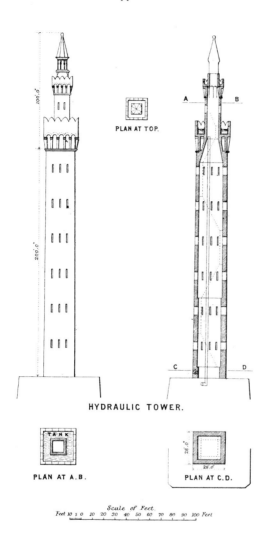

PLAN AT TOP.

HYDRAULIC TOWER.

PLAN AT A.B.

PLAN AT C.D.

Scale of Feet.
Feet 10 5 0   10   20   30   40   50   60   70   80   90   100 Feet

Fig. A.2   GRIMSBY WATER TOWER

'Here for the first time an independent water supply system was laid down solely for the distribution of water power for the working of mechanical appliances at the docks.' – E. B. Ellington, Past President, Institution of Mechanical Engineers, Thomas Hawksley Lecture, 1913.

tower along the same lines as the Grimsby Tower but the ground at New Holland was incapable of supporting the weight so he was forced to find an alternative. Finally he devised the hydraulic accumulator, so named because its function was to accumulate excess energy developed by the pump against a sudden above-average demand. The accumulator had previously been mooted by Bramah (it was in effect a hydraulic press in reverse), but Lord Armstrong was the first to put the idea into practice. Compared with the storage tower the accumulator could store only a very small volume of water but it permitted the use of a much higher working pressure, the pressure used at New Holland corresponding to a head of 1500 ft. Such pressures were out of the question with storage towers so with the advent of the accumulator the storage tower was no longer a practical proposition and the era of high-pressure hydraulics commenced. The Grimsby Water Tower was virtually obsolete almost as soon as it became operational. Today it supports a television relay mast.

A.5 CONVERSION FACTORS AND USEFUL APPROXIMATIONS

Quantity
One litre of water weighs one kilogram = 2·2 lb.
One gallon of water weighs 10 lb.
One gallon = 4·5 litres.
One cubic foot of water weighs 62·5 lb.

Pressure
1 kg/cm² = 10 metres of water = 32·8 feet of water = 14·2 lb/in².
1 lb/in² = 2·304 feet of water.

Power
At a pressure of 725 lb/in² (51 kg/cm²):
Every two gallons (9 litres) of water pumped per minute represents approximately one horsepower (more correctly 1·01 h.p.).
One horsepower-hour = 118·5 gallons.
One killowatt-hour = 158·8 gallons.
1000 gallons = 6·29 kWh.
Other heads and quantities pro rata.

Costs

1p = 2·4d.   5p = 1s.

1s per 1000 gallons at 725 lb/in² = 0·794p or approximately 0·8p per kWh.

A.6 FLOW OF WATER IN PIPES

The flow of water through a pipe or channel will be resisted by friction between the water and the inner surface of the pipe or channel and this friction is dependent upon the nature and condition of the surface. The subject is discussed at length in standard works on hydraulics. It will suffice here to say that many formulae for the calculation of the resulting loss of pressure or equivalent head have been evolved by a combination of theory and experiment. One of the best known of these is that known as Darcy's equation.

Darcy, in 1857, as a result of a large number of experiments found that the loss of head due to friction was proportional to the length of the pipe, to the square of the velocity of flow, and inversely proportional to the pipe diameter, i.e., the head lost in friction, denoted by h = constant $\times \, lv^2/d$ where l is the length of the pipe, d its diameter, and v the velocity of flow.

In seeking a general formula applicable to both pipes and channels it is necessary in the case of a channel to find a linear dimension to use in place of d. The most convenient is what has become known as the hydraulic mean depth which is the ratio of the cross-sectional area of the flow to the wetted perimeter and is usually denoted by the letter m. In the case of a circular pipe $m = d/4$. Also, it is convenient to express quantities involved in hydraulic calculations in terms of kinetic energy of unit mass of the fluid, i.e., $v^2/(2g)$, so Darcy's equation takes the final form of

$$h = \frac{fl}{m} \cdot \frac{v^2}{2g}$$

for a channel, and

$$\frac{4fl}{d} \cdot \frac{v^2}{2g}$$

for a pipe, where f is a constant the value of which depends on the nature of the wetted surface and is determined experimentally or from existing data.

In the absence of other data the following values can be used:

$$f = 0.005 \left(1 + \frac{1}{12d}\right) \text{for new pipes.}$$

$$f = 0.01 \left(1 + \frac{1}{12d}\right) \text{for old and encrusted pipes.}$$

d = diameter of pipe in feet.

Darcy's equation is simple, convenient and in common use but it must be remembered that the value of f, and consequently the rate of flow, can vary appreciably, particularly with temperature.

As an example, consider a pipe one mile (5280 ft) long, 6 in (0.5 ft) diameter, velocity of flow 2·5 ft/s. f for a new pipe works out at 0·0058 and the head lost in friction comes out at 23·77 ft of water or 10·32 lb/in². This example will be of interest when we later consider efficiency of transmission. As the loss of head varies as the square of the velocity of flow when transmitting power it is necessary to keep the velocity as low as possible. The value chosen will depend on the permissible loss of head and the distance the power has to be transmitted. The rate of flow in the public hydraulic supply mains was from 2·5 to 4 ft/s, the latter being the value for London.

A.7 EFFICIENCY OF POWER TRANSMISSION

This subject already referred to on p. 10 is discussed here in greater depth. If H is the head of water leaving the station, station pressure $p = wH$ where w is the weight per unit volume. If H is in feet, w the weight of a cubic foot of water, in pounds, p will be in pounds per square foot. Head of water at the consumer's premises $= H$ minus the head lost in friction, that is,

$$H - \frac{4flv^2}{2gd},$$

and the energy available per second to the consumer will be (the weight of water per second) × (available head), or

$$E = \frac{\pi d^2}{4} wv \left(H - \frac{4flv^2}{2gd}\right) = \frac{\pi d^2}{4} w \left(Hv - \frac{4flv^3}{2gd}\right)$$

This will be a maximum when

$$\frac{dE}{dv} = 0 \ \text{ or } H = \frac{3flv^2}{2gd} \ \text{ or } H = 3h$$

that is, the head lost in friction is one-third of the head at the station. Since the efficiency of transmission is $(H - h)/H$, when maximum power is being transmitted the efficiency of transmission is only 66·6 per cent. The energy leaving the station per second is

$$E = H \cdot \frac{\pi}{4} d^2 wv \ \text{ or } w^2 p \frac{\pi}{4} d^2 v$$

where p is the station pressure.
    Hence

$$v = \frac{E \cdot 4}{\pi w^2 p d^2} \tag{1}$$

The loss of energy due to friction per second is

$$\frac{4flv^2}{2gd} \times \text{(weight of water flowing per second.)}$$

$$= \frac{4flv^2}{2gd} \cdot \frac{\pi d^2}{4} wv$$

$$= \frac{4fl\pi wd^2}{2g \cdot 4d} v^3$$

and substituting for v from (1)

$$= \frac{32fl}{w^5 \pi^2} \left(\frac{E^3}{p^3 d^5}\right)$$

So the loss of energy due to friction varies as $1/(p^3 d^5)$ and the efficiency of transmission will be greatest when the energy lost in friction is the least, that is when p and d are as large as practicable.

The extent to which the diameter can be increased depends upon the overall cost including manufacture, excavation work, and laying. In practice a size of main which gave a pressure drop of 10 lb/in^2 per mile was found to give the most economical results (see p. 10 and example p. 11), the pipes being duplicated for larger powers.

Increasing the working pressure necessitates an increase in the thickness of the pipe wall, increases the difficulty of effective joint sealing, and calls for more robust generating plant.

Working pressures in the region of 700 lb/in^2 became popular because this was the pressure adopted by Lord Armstrong and his lead was followed by equipment and mains manufacturers, and consequently this was the working pressure about which there was considerable accumulated experience. But demands for power for pressing led to the adoption of a working pressure of half a ton per square inch at both Manchester and Glasgow. The tendency was to regard this pressure as the upper limit for transmission purposes, any exceptional demands for a higher pressure being met by the use of intensifiers on consumers' premises.

A.8 PIPE MATERIALS

Cast iron, at one time the most suitable material, was in common use for hydraulic supply mains, but due to its low working stress, the internal diameter of a cast-iron pipe cannot be very high unless the pipe is of appreciable thickness. For a pressure of 1000 lb/in^2 a diameter greater than 8 in (20 cm) results in an excessively thick pipe. The stress cannot be assumed constant across the thickness and such pipes have to be designed in accordance with thick cylinder theory.

Steel has become a much more suitable material for use at very high pressures as not only is its working stress much higher resulting in a much thinner pipe for a given diameter and working pressure but it has a greater resistance to shock than cast iron. In later years some of the hydraulic mains in London were replaced by steel pipes.

The type of flanged joint in common use for the cast-iron pipes is shown in Fig. A.3.

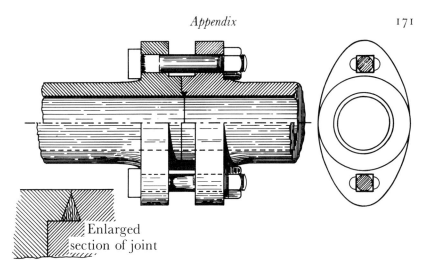

Enlarged
section of joint

Fig. A.3   STANDARD JOINT FOR CAST IRON HYDRAULIC SUPPLY MAINS

Reading and Reference List

BOOKS AND PAMPHLETS

A. H. Gibson. *Hydraulics and its applications*, Third edition, 1925 (Constable & Co, London)

F. C. Lea. *Hydraulics for engineers and engineering students*, Fourth edition, 1926 (Edward Arnold & Co, London)

G. Croydon Marks. *Hydraulic machinery employed in the concentration and transmission of power*, 1891 (The Technical Publishing Co, London)

Henry Robinson. *Hydraulic power and hydraulic machinery*, 1887

Anon. *Manchester Corporation Water works hydraulic supply*, 1926 (Manchester Corporation)

Robert Hunter. *The water supply of Glasgow*, 1933 (Glasgow Corporation)

Anon. *Public hydraulic power*, 1896 (Melbourne Hydraulic Power Co)

B. Pugh. *Positive Rotary Pumps, compressors and exhausters*, 1936 (Draughtsman Publishing Co, London)

Anon. *Hydraulic pumps and motors for machine tools*, 1958 (Yellow back series, Machinery Publishing Co, London)

Anon. *Hydraulic circuits for machine tools*, 1962 (Yellow back series, Machinery Publishing Co, London)

R. J. Law. *The Steam Engine*, (Science Museum booklet, London)

A. Privat Deschanel. *Elementary Treatise on Natural Philosophy*, translated and edited by J. D. Everett, Sixth edition, 1881 (Blackie & Son, London)

Bryan Donkin. *Gas, Oil and Air Engines*, 1911 (Chas. Griffin & Co, London)

ARTICLES IN PERIODICALS

'The Transmission of Energy by Compressed Air', *Engineering*, **7**, 21, 28 June 1889

'Hydraulic power in Hull', *The port of Hull and its facilities for trade* 1907, p. 193 (East Yorks Publishing Co)

'The Glasgow water power station', *Glasgow Herald*, 30 May 1895
'Hydraulic power and its grievances', *Liverpool Review*, 9 February 1889
Anthony Clark, 'The Lincoln Gas Light and Coke Co', *Lincolnshire Industrial Archaeology* 1969, **4** (No. 2), 43 (Lincolnshire Local History Society)

PROCEEDINGS OF PROFESSIONAL INSTITUTIONS, SOCIETIES, ETC.

Proceedings of the Institution of Civil Engineers
1876–7. Sir W. G. Armstrong. 'The history of the modern development of water pressure machinery'
Henry Robinson. 'The transmission of power to distances'
1887–8. Edward B. Ellington. 'The distribution of hydraulic power in London'
1893. Edward B. Ellington. 'Hydraulic power supplies in London'
1864–5. Edward Hele Clark. 'The development of the Great Grimsby (Royal) docks'

Proceedings of the Institution of Mechanical Engineers
1858. Sir W. G. Armstrong. 'On water pressure machinery'
1868. Sir W. G. Armstrong. 'On the transmission of power by water pressure with applications to railway goods stations, forge and foundry cranes, and furnace hoists'
1895. Edward B. Ellington. 'Hydraulic power supply in towns, Glasgow, Manchester, Buenos Ayres, etc.'
1913 Edward B. Ellington. 'Water as a mechanical agent'. Thomas Hawksley Memorial Lecture
1928. C. J. T. Billingham. 'Hydraulic power'

Proceedings of the Engineering Society of New South Wales
1888–9. Norman Selfe. 'The operation of power companies and power transmission by compressed air'
1894. Tom Dickinson. 'Notes on the hydraulic power supply in Sydney'

Transactions of Liverpool Engineering Society
1903. F. J. Haswell. 'Hydraulic machinery'

Transactions of Mason College of Engineering Society
1893. Henry Lea. 'The Birmingham hydraulic supply station'

The British Association

1886. J. Sturgeon. 'The Birmingham compressed air scheme'. Birmingham meeting, 8 Sept 1886.

Index

Accumulator, hydraulic, 3
Advantages of hydraulic power, 5, 13
Air preheating, 31
Antwerp lighting system, 140
Appreciation of work of supply companies, 6
Argand burner, 25
Armstrong, Sir William, later Lord, 3, 17

Batswing gas burner, 25
Bellis steam engine, 142
Birmingham Compressed Air System, 29, 32
Birmingham Hydraulic Supply, 128–130
Boilers, 52
Brotherhood engine, 83
Brunel, I. K., 4
Bunsen burner, 25

Cage counterbalancing (lifts), 69
Carbon filament lamp, 18
Cellar pumps, 85, 89
Central electricity stations, 145
Centralized hydraulic power system, 149
Centrifugal pumps, 147
City Road Station, 112
Clarke's electric machine, 19
Coal gas, 24, 25
Compound engines, 43, 44
Compound engine types, 46
Compound Pumping Engine, early three-
    cylinder, 49
Commutator, 20, 21
Compressed Air Systems, 30
Compressed Air Clock, 34
Condensing Plant, 56
Consumers' Meters, 63
Cornish Boiler, 52
Crane, hydraulic, 75

Darcy's Equation, 8, 167
Dates of inauguration (hydraulic stations),
    44
Deep well pump, 107
Domestic water supply, use of, 14
Double-acting ram and piston pump, 60

Early electric power stations, 38
Economizers, 56
Edison, T. A., 17
Efficiency of transmission, 10, 11, 168
Eggborough Power Station, 152
Electricity Grid, 145
Electrification of hydraulic stations, 167
Electric Light Stations, 16
Ellington, E. B., 95
Extractor pump, 57

Factory lighting, 17
Fairbairn–Beeley boiler, 54
Falcon Wharf Station, 100, 103
Fire hydrants, 87, 88
Flow of water through pipes, 8, 167
Fowler, Sir John, 3
Frictional resistance to flow, 7, 8, 167, 168

Gas burners, 25
Gas engine, 26
Gas lighting, 15
Gas Light and Coke Co, 25
Gas mantle, 26
Gas Referees, 25
Galloway tubes, 53
Glasgow Electricity Supply, 143
Glasgow Hydraulic Power, 115–122
Gramme dynamo, 23, 24
Greathead Fire hydrant, 88
Grimsby Docks, 2, 4, 164
Grosvenor Road Station, 101

Haswell, F. J., 96
High voltage transmission, 147
Hoists, 67
Horizontal pumping engine sizes, 47
Hornsby Ackroyd engine, 29
Hot air engines, 160
Hull Hydraulic Power Station, 91–96
Humber ferry terminal, 3
Hydraulic accumulator, 61
Hydraulic balance for lifts, 69–73
Hydraulic engines, 81

Incandescent electric lamp, 17
Integral hydraulic supply, 148
Intensifier, 80
Intensity of hydraulic pressure, 7

Jet pump, 85, 86
Jigger, hydraulic, 74
Jigger, two power, 77

Kennedy, Sir Alexander B. W., 39
Kent water meter, 65, 66
Kingston upon Hull Corporation, 91

Lancashire boiler, 53
Lenoir engine, 27
Lifts, 67
Liverpool Hydraulic Power, 112–115
London Hydraulic Power Co, 96–112
Loss of head (due to friction), 8, 168–169

Magneto electric machine, 19
Manchester Hydraulic Power, 122–128
Machine shop practice, 89
Melbourne Hydraulic Supply, 131, 132
Millbank Station, 101, 106, 109
Murdock, William, 25

New Holland hydraulic station, 4
New York steam supply, 30

Oil engines, 28, 29
Oscillating engine, 82
Osmium filament lamp, 18
Otto engine, 28

Pacinotti's Ring Armature Machine, 22
Paris Compressed Air System, 34–38
Parkinson's Water Meter, 64
Parsons, Sir Charles, 39, 45
Parsons' turbine, 45
Pelton wheel, 5, 67, 156
Pixii's electric machine, 19

Planing machine, hydraulic, 89
Popp, Victor, 34
Positive rotary pumps, 147
Power generation and transmission, 1, 15
Power storage, 13
Power transmission by ropes, 2
Priestman oil engine, 28
Pump drives, 5
Pumping engine, 42
Pumping engine types, 43
Pump types, 57
Preece, W. H., 40
Presses, 78
Price of electricity, 40, 157, 158

Ram pump, 59
Ramsbottom engine, 81
Reciprocating pump types, 59
Rigg Hydraulic Engine, 84, 85
Ring armature, 22
Robinson, Henry, 95
Rotherhithe Station, 101, 112

Saxton's electric machine, 19
Siemens's armature, 21
Slide valve, 43
South Wales Electric Power Co, 143, 160
Sprinkler fire fighting systems, 88
Station size, 13
Steam power, 29
Swan, Joseph, 17

Table engine, 160
Tantalum filament lamp, 18
Three-throw ram pump, 59
Triple expansion engines, 43, 44
Tweddell, R. H., 90, 95

Upper Boat Power Station, 150

Vicars' mechanical stoker, 54

Wall crane, 77
Wapping Power Station, 101–112
Water measurement, 62
Welsbach, C. A. von, 26
Wetted perimeter, 8, 10, 11
Wharf cranes, 78
Wheatstone, Sir Charles, 21
Willans engine, 142
Wire rope lifts, 72
Working pressure, 8, 10, 11, 169